REWARD

REWARD

Elementary

Resource Pack

Communicative activities for students of English

Susan Kay
The Lake School of English

MACMILLAN
HEINEMANN
English Language Teaching

Macmillan Heinemann English Language Teaching
Between Towns Road, Oxford OX4 3PP

A division of Macmillan Publishers Limited

Companies and representatives throughout the world

ISBN 0 435 24249 0

Text © Susan Kay and The Lake School of English 1997
Design and illustration © Macmillan Publishers Limited 1998
First published 1997

Heinemann is a registered trademark of Reed Educational & Professional
Publishing Limited

Designed by D&J Hunter
Cover design by Stafford & Stafford
Illustrations by Nancy Anderson, Cathy Balme, Kathy Baxendale,
Peter Bull, Joan Corlass, David Eaton, Maggie Ling, Gillian Martin,
Ed McLauchlan, Julia Pearson, Simon Smith and Gary Wing.

Author's acknowledgements

Thanks…
- to all the teachers at The Lake School for trying out the activities and
  giving individual feedback.
- to Alyson Maskell for her thorough and efficient editing.
- to Jenny Hunter and the illustrators for bringing the worksheets to life.
- to Simon Greenall, Catherine Smith and Angela Reckitt for their
  support.

Printed and bound in Great Britain by Martins the Printers Ltd, Berwick-upon-Tweed

2003 2002 2001 2000
10 9 8 7 6 5

Contents

Worksheet	Interaction	Skills	Activity	Time (mins)	Grammar and functions	Vocabulary
1 *Stress dominoes*	Groupwork	Speaking	Game	20	Saying the names of countries	Names of countries
2 *Visiting cards*	Whole class	Speaking	Communication task: introducing people	10–15	Present simple *to be* *a/an* Introductions	Jobs, nationalities
3a and 3b *Friends*	Pairwork	Speaking	Asking and answering questions	20	Giving personal information Questions without a question word Negatives Short answers	Personal information
4a and 4b *Memory test*	Pairwork Groupwork	Speaking	Memorise and describe	20	*There is/are* *How many ...?*	Office vocabulary
5 *Where is it?*	Whole class	Speaking	Asking and saying where things are	15	Prepositions of place: *in, on, under, near*	Personal possessions
Progress check 1–5 *Have you got it?*	Whole class	Speaking	Asking and answering questions	30–40	*Has/have got* *Have you got ...?* Short answers *Yes, I have./No, I haven't.*	Personal information Personal possessions
6 *Photo album*	Groupwork	Speaking	Talking about the family	20	Possessive *'s*	Members of the family
7 *When and what?*	Pairwork	Writing Speaking	Asking and answering questions	20	Present simple for routines Prepositions of time	Routine activities
8a and 8b *Spot the similarities*	Pairwork	Speaking Writing	Asking and answering questions and writing descriptions	30	Describing rooms *There is/are* *Is there ...? Are there ...?* *Some* and *any*	Rooms and furniture
9 *Habits*	Whole class	Writing Speaking	Completing a chart and asking and answering questions	20–30	Present simple for habits and routines *Wh-* questions *How do you ...?* 3rd person singular	Routine activities
10 *Sentences in a hat*	Whole class	Speaking	Completing unfinished sentences and asking and answering questions	20	Talking about likes and dislikes	Everyday and leisure activities
Progress check 6–10a and 6–10b *Mix and match*	Groupwork	Reading Speaking	Board game	30	Verb and noun collocations	Everyday activities
11 *Daily routine*	Pairwork	Speaking	Questionnaire	20	Present simple: asking how often Short answers Adverbs of frequency	Everyday actions
12 *Travel*	Pairwork	Writing Speaking	Putting words in order and asking and answering questions	30	Present simple questions Talking about travel	Means of transport
13 *Can you make a cake?*	Whole class	Speaking	Mill drill	15	*Can you ...?* *Yes, I can./No, I can't.*	Everyday and leisure activities
14a and 14b *Where can I buy some bread?*	Pairwork	Speaking	Asking and saying where places are	20	*Where can I ...?* *There's a ...* Prepositions of place Asking for and giving directions	Shops and town facilities
15 *What am I doing?*	Whole class	Speaking	Miming	30	Present continuous	Everyday and leisure activities
Progress check 11–15a and 11–15b *Spot the differences*	Pairwork	Speaking	Asking and answering questions	20	*There is/are ..., Is/Are there ...?* *How many ...?* *Some* and *any* Prepositions of place Present continuous The article	General
16 *How was your holiday?*	Whole class	Speaking	Mill drill	15	*Was/were* *What was it like?*	Words associated with holidays
17a *Health survey*	Whole class	Speaking	Survey	30	Countable and uncountable nouns *Some* and *any*	Food and drink
17b *What shall we do?*	Whole class	Speaking	Mill drill	20	Asking for and making suggestions	Leisure activities
18 *Poor Fabio*	Groupwork	Speaking Reading	Picture story	30–40	Past simple: regular verbs	General
19 *What are you like?*	Groupwork	Writing	Writing a description	30	Talking about appearance	Adjectives to describe appearance and character Physical features
20 *A holiday*	Pairwork	Speaking	Guessing and checking predictions	30	Past simple: irregular verbs *Yes/no* questions and short answers	Irregular verbs Verbs associated with holidays

Worksheet	Interaction	Skills	Activity	Time (mins)	Grammar and functions	Vocabulary
Progress check 16–20 *Find out*	Whole class	Speaking	Asking and answering questions	20	Simple past:regular and irregular verbs *Yes/no* questions Countable and uncountable nouns *Some* and *any*	General
21a and 21b *John Lennon*	Pairwork	Reading Writing Speaking	Writing, asking and answering questions to complete a text	50–60	Past simple *Wh-* questions	Life history
22 *Find someone who...*	Whole class	Speaking	Completing a chart	20–30	Dates Expressions of time	General
23 *What are their names?*	Groupwork	Speaking	Describing people	20	Describing people Present continuous or present simple Actions of the face, hands and body	Items of clothing
24 *What am I going to do?*	Whole class	Speaking	Miming	30	*Going to* + infinitive	Everyday and leisure activities
25 *I'd like an ice cream, please*	Whole class	Speaking	Mill drill	15	Offers and requests *Would like* Asking and saying how much	Food and drink
Progress check 21–25 *When did you last...?*	Whole class	Speaking	Asking and answering questions	15–20	Simple past: irregular verbs *Wh-* questions Expressions of time	Everyday and leisure activities
26 *Snap!*	Pairwork	Reading Speaking	Game	10–15	Collocation	Items of shopping
27a and 27b *Lost and found*	Groupwork	Speaking	A describing game	20	Describing objects	Adjectives to describe objects Materials
28 *Ouch!*	Pairwork Groupwork	Writing Speaking	Writing complaints about health and advice	30	Asking and saying how you feel: *I feel ..., My ... hurts, I've got ...* Sympathising and giving advice: *should, shouldn't*	Adjectives to describe how you feel Nouns for illnesses
29a and 29b *World quiz*	Groupwork	Speaking	Game	30	Comparative and superlative forms of short adjectives	World facts
30 *Find the person with the most...*	Whole class	Speaking	Asking and answering questions	15–20	Comparative and superlative forms of longer adjectives	Adjectives to describe people, everyday activities and leisure activities
Progress check 26–30 *Think of a word*	Groupwork	Writing Speaking	Game	30	Comparative forms	General
31 *Guess the place*	Whole class	Writing Speaking	Writing and guessing	20	*Must, mustn't*	General
32 *Have you ever...?*	Groupwork	Writing Speaking	Game	60	Present perfect to talk about experiences Past simple to talk about a definite time in the past	Past participles of regular and irregular verbs
33 *I've just...*	Whole class	Speaking	Mill drill	15	Present perfect to talk about recent events: *just* and *yet*	General
34 *Purposeful activities*	Whole class	Speaking	Asking and answering questions	15–20	Infinitive of purpose	Routine activities
35 *I do it my way*	Pairwork	Writing Speaking	Guessing	20	Adverbs	Adverbs Everyday activities
Progress check 31–35 *Crossword*	Pairwork	Speaking Writing	Crossword	40	Infinitive of purpose	Everyday objects Places
36 *Travel dominoes*	Groupwork	Speaking	Game	15	Collocation	Words associated with rail and air travel
37 *Predictogram*	Whole class	Writing Speaking	Game	30	Future simple for predictions Instructions	General
38 *Did you know...?*	Groupwork	Speaking Reading	Matching two halves of sentences	20–30	Present and past passive	Inventions and other world facts
39a and 39b *Class survey*	Pairwork Groupwork	Speaking Writing	Survey	30–40	Reported speech: statements *... said that* + clause	General
40 *Tell your group...*	Groupwork	Speaking	Board game	30	Tense review	General
Progress check 36–40 *Find the mistake*	Pairwork	Speaking	Identifying and correcting mistakes	30	Revision	Revision

Notes for teachers

The Resource Pack

This Resource Pack for teachers contains about 50 communicative practice activities for Elementary students. It is designed to be used with *Reward* Elementary Student's Book, but can be used to supplement any course.

There is a wide range of activities, which provide practice in speaking, reading and writing. All the activities have been tried and tested many times in the classroom.

You can use the activities in different ways:
- to extend lessons from *Reward* Elementary Student's Book
- to revise specific structures, language or vocabulary later in the course
- to supplement any course

If you are using *Reward* Elementary Student's Book

The Resource Pack provides at least one practice activity for each Lesson and Progress check. The numbers on the Worksheets correspond to the lessons in the Student's Book.

If you are not using *Reward* Student's Book

Use the contents chart at the front of the Resource Pack to select the activity you want to use.

How to use the Resource Pack

Each activity in the Resource Pack consists of one photocopiable worksheet, with Teacher's Notes on the back. (Occasionally there are two worksheets for an activity.)

The worksheets in the Resource Pack are hole-punched for filing. When you have selected the activity you want to use, carefully detach it from the pack, and check the Teacher's Notes to find out how long the activity will take, and what preparation is required. The Teacher's Notes provide step-by-step guidance, ensuring that less experienced teachers, or those with little time to spend on preparation, can use the activities easily.

The worksheets have been designed for maximum clarity, even when photocopied. However, if you have the facilities to enlarge your photocopies, you may find this useful, especially in the case of pictures or board games.

Some of the worksheets require cutting up into cards (for example, dominoes, mill drills, bingo). We suggest that you stick the photocopies onto card before cutting them up. Laminating cards will also give them a longer classroom life. When cutting up the worksheets, remember to cut up the photocopy and not the original! Put the original in a folder or ring-binder, or put it back in the pack. Once you have cut the cards out, put them into envelopes and write the title and activity and the number of cards on the front of the envelope.

Some activities require multiple sets of cards. With these, it is a good idea, when you photocopy each set, to put a different mark, or use a different coloured pen on the back of each set. This will avoid confusion should the sets become mixed up, and will also make it easier for you to check the number of copies per set. Store each set in an envelope, as above.

Mill drills

There are several mill drills in the Resource Pack. You can also use some of the cards from other activities for mill drills.

What is a mill drill?

A mill drill is an interactive way of drilling newly-presented language, using cards with picture or word prompts on one or both sides. It fulfils the function of repetition and substitution drills. As the name suggests, the students stand up and 'mill' (circulate) around the class, interacting with several partners. A mill drill is an ideal way of providing controlled practice of a new structure or function after initial presentation, because it gives students the opportunity to repeat the same language with several different partners.

The benefits of a mill drill... for the student

The presentation stage of a lesson can be rather teacher-centred and static. A mill drill makes a welcome change of focus for both students and teacher. It makes controlled practice more communicative and enjoyable for students and basic repetition becomes more stimulating and active. A mill drill can also be reassuring for less confident students, not only because the students are solely dependent on mechanical repetition and substitution, but also because they are not required to speak out alone.

The benefits of a mill drill... for the teacher

Mill drills differ from conventional drills in that they are student-centred, providing an invaluable opportunity for the teacher to monitor individual students' weaknesses, particularly pronunciation and intonation.

How to do a mill drill with your class

There are instructions for each mill drill in the Teacher's Notes on the back of each mill-drill worksheet. The basic procedure for doing a mill drill is as follows:

Preparation

1 Photocopy the worksheet and cut out the cards as indicated. With a large class, divide the class into groups and make one copy of the worksheet for each group.

2 Give each student a card. It is not necessary to use all the cards on the worksheet, so if there are fewer students in the class or group than the number of cards on the worksheet, leave out the surplus number. Some cards have a prompt on one side only, while others have prompts on both sides, so follow the instructions in the Teacher's Notes carefully.

Demonstration

1 Tell the students that they are going to spend 10 to 15 minutes practising the new language and that you are going to demonstrate this.

2 Give one card to each student in the class, and keep one for yourself. Select a sample dialogue (as suggested in the Teacher's Notes on the back of the worksheet), and write it on the board, preferably eliciting the language from the students. Indicate the part of the dialogue to be supplied by the picture or word prompt on the card.
For example:

A: *Do you like reading?*
B: *Yes, I do.*
A: *So do I.*

3 Explain that this language will change according to the prompt on the card, and elicit suggestions for this.
For example:
Do you like reading?
       playing tennis?
       writing letters?

4 Show the students how to hold their cards. This is important because double-sided cards must be held in such a way that when students are talking to a partner, they are both able to see each other's cards.

The correct way to hold a double-sided card.

ORDER

The wrong way to hold a double-sided card.

CHAOS

5 Choose a confident or extrovert student to demonstrate the activity with you. Then ask two or three pairs of students to demonstrate the dialogue.

Students do the mill drill

Ask all the students to stand up and to go round the class or group, repeating the dialogue with as many different partners as possible, and using their cards as prompts.

Some mill drills have two stages involving either turning the cards round, or exchanging cards with another student, so that students get the opportunity to make new responses. In these mill drills, tell the students that they should stop talking when you clap your hands and continue once they have made the necessary change.

A mill drill is a controlled practice activity and it is important that students use the language accurately. Therefore, while the students are doing the mill drill, you should circulate, listening and correcting students' mistakes in grammar and pronunciation.

Pair forming

The picture cards on some of the worksheets can be used for a pair-forming activity, as follows.

1 Make two copies of the worksheet and cut out the pictures so that there are two identical pictures for each pair of students in the class.
2 Shuffle the cards and give them out to the students. Tell the students not to show their cards to anyone else. The students then stand up and go around the class, asking and answering questions about their pictures until they find the student who has the identical card.

You can use this activity as a way of putting students into pairs for another activity. You can put students into groups in a similar way, by making copies of the same picture for each student in a group.

Pelmanism

The picture cards on some of the worksheets can be used for pelmanism (a matching game) as follows:

1 Make one set of cards for each pair (or small group) of students and give each group the cards and an equal number of blank cards. For example, if there are 12 picture cards, give the group 12 blank cards.
2 Ask the students to write a sentence on each blank card to match a picture card.

For example:

picture card   sentence

She's a pilot.

3 When they have done this, ask the students to spread out the pictures face down, and spread out the sentences face down, separately from the pictures.
4 Now ask the students to take it in turns to turn over one picture card and one sentence. If the two cards match, the student can keep them, and play again. If they do not match, the student turns them back over, and the next player repeats the procedure.
5 The game continues in this way until all the cards have been used up. The winner is the student with the most cards.

12B	1A
	ITALY

1B	2A
■ ... ■	**SWEDEN**

2B	3A
■ ■	**BRAZIL**

3B	4A
■ ■	**AMERICA**

4B	5A
■ ■ ■ ■	**GERMANY**

5B	6A
	DENMARK

6B	7A
	UKRAINE

7B	8A
	AUSTRALIA

8B	9A
	PORTUGAL

9B	10A
	CHINA

10B	11A
	JAPAN

11B	12A
	BULGARIA

Stress dominoes Worksheet

ACTIVITY
Groupwork: speaking

AIM
To play a game of dominoes by matching names of countries with their stress patterns.

GRAMMAR AND FUNCTIONS
Saying the names of countries

VOCABULARY
Names of countries

PREPARATION
Make one copy of the worksheet for each group of three students. Provide scissors for each group.

TIME
20 minutes

PROCEDURE
1 Ask the students to call out the names of the countries they come from and write them on the board. If you have a monocultural class, ask them to call out any names of countries around the world. Write the relevant stress patterns next to each name.

2 Ask the students to work in groups of three.

3 Give one copy of the worksheet to each group and ask them to choose one member of the group to do the writing.

4 Explain that they are going to play a game of dominoes but that before they can start, they have to write in the stress patterns for the names of the countries in boxes 5 to 12. Point out the way the dominoes are arranged and explain that they are numbered on the worksheet to show which name goes with which stress pattern. Demonstrate this using the examples which are already filled in on the worksheet.

5 Now ask the students to work in their groups, writing the stress patterns in the boxes marked 'B' on their worksheet. While they are doing this, go round to each group and check that their stress patterns are correct. Answer questions and offer help.

The correct answers are:

5B and 9B ■ ■ ■

6B and 10B ■ ■

7B and 11B ■ ■

8B and 12B ■ ■ ■ ■

6 When they have finished and you are satisfied that their stress patterns are correct, give each group a pair of scissors and ask them to cut the dominoes out as indicated. Make sure that students cut off the numbers above the dominoes.

7 Before they start their game of dominoes, explain how to play, using the instructions below.

8 The students are ready to play the game. While they are playing, go round to each group and check they are playing correctly.

9 When they have finished one game, they can shuffle and play again.

OPTION
Ask the students to add some dominoes of their own using some of the countries you wrote on the board in procedure point 1. Make sure that for every country there is a matching stress pattern and that matching pairs are on separate dominoes as on the worksheet.

HOW TO PLAY THE GAME

1 Shuffle the dominoes.

2 Players take four dominoes each.

3 Player A puts down any one of their dominoes face up.

4 The player on Player A's left (Player B) must then put down one of their dominoes, making sure that the name on their domino matches the stress pattern, or the stress pattern on their domino matches the name, on Player A's domino.

5 The players take it in turns to add dominoes in this way.

6 If a player cannot put down one of their dominoes, they miss a turn.

7 The first player to get rid of all of their dominoes is the winner.

Av. Barcelona 22, Malgrat de Mar, Spain

Ms Ana
G O M E Z
Film Director

tel (93) 761 02 55   fax (93) 761 02 57

Mr TAKU MIYAZAKI
ARTIST

1-37-12 Ikebukiro Houcho, Toshima-Ku, TOKYO, JAPAN
☎ 03-3982-6511

Mr Mauricio CHAGAS
(musician)

*Rua Marichal Mascarenhas de Moraes 161/402
Copacabana, Rio de Janeiro, RJ – BRAZIL*
21.523.5100

Mr Andreas Hiepler
Accountant

Budapester str 45, 10787 BERLIN, Germany
Tel/Fax: (49) 30 269 91 31

Ms PAWINEE PAPORN
(Travel Agent)

9/32 Charan sanit wong 47 Rd
BANGKOK
THAILAND
(02) 434 3350

Ms Francesca Riva

Journalist

Viale V. Emanuele, 3 – 24100 Bergamo – ITALY

Tel (39) 035 25 68 72   Fax (39) 035 24 38 22

Am Guggenberg 10, 8053 Zürich, SWITZERLAND

Ms LUCY KASER
Taxi Driver

Tel 01/381 88 23

**Mr ROBERT
ALLEN**

ACTOR

11 Horbury Cres.,
London W11
UK
Tel 0171 346 7780

Ms Jane Baker
English Teacher

• • •

112 Sydney Rd, Fawkner, Melbourne, AUSTRALIA
Tel: (61) 3 534 0524

Mr Simon Shepherd
Engineer

101 5th Avenue, Los Angeles
USA

Tel: (310) 245 1122

PHOTOCOPIABLE

Visiting cards Worksheet **2**

ACTIVITY
Whole class: speaking

AIM
To introduce people to one another, giving personal information.

GRAMMAR AND FUNCTIONS
Present simple *to be*
a/an
Introductions

VOCABULARY
Jobs, nationalities

PREPARATION
Make one copy of the worksheet for each group of up to nine students and cut it up into cards as indicated. There are five cards with male names (Mr) and five with female names (Ms) for you to choose from. If there are more students in your class than there are cards of one sex, change the first names and title on the appropriate number of cards before you give them to the students. Keep one card for yourself to demonstrate the activity.

TIME
10 to 15 minutes

PROCEDURE
1 If there are more than nine students in the class, divide them into groups. (Within those groups, the students will be working mainly in threes.) Give one card to each student in the class.

2 Tell the students that they are now the person on their visiting card and that they are going to practise introducing people to one another. Tell them that the title is there to indicate whether the person is male (Mr) or female (Ms) but they don't have to say the title when they introduce the person.

3 Write an example dialogue on the board:
This is my friend Ana Gomez. She's from Spain. She's a film director.

4 Demonstrate the activity with two students. Write on the board:
Student A introduces Student B.
Student B introduces Student C.
Student C introduces Student A.

For the demonstration, you are Student A and your two partners are Student B and Student C. Ask them to hold their visiting cards up, facing out. Read the information on Student B's visiting card and introduce him/her to Student C. Students B and C should then shake hands and say *Hello.* When you have done that, ask Student B to introduce Student C to you. Shake hands with Student C and say *Hello.* Next, ask Student C to introduce you to Student B. Shake hands with Student B and say *Hello.*

5 Now ask the students to work with two other students from their group and to decide who is A, B and C. If the class does not divide exactly into groups of three, make up the numbers with groups of four.

6 Ask the students to hold their visiting cards up and take it in turns to introduce one another.

7 When they have finished, ask them to form new groups of three with two different students and repeat the activity. Make sure they all have different identities.

8 Repeat procedure point 7.

OPTION (1)
You can do this activity with the students sitting down in a circle. Moving round the circle in a clockwise direction, each student introduces the student on their right to the student on their left.

OPTION (2)
Students introduce themselves to everybody in the class, using the information on their own visiting cards:
I'm Ana Gomez. I'm from Spain and I'm a film director.

FIRST NAME   1) _____   2) _____   3) _____

Job _____ _____ _____

Age _____ _____ _____

Surname _____ _____ _____

Where from? _____ _____ _____

Married? _____ _____ _____

PHOTOCOPIABLE

Friends Worksheets ③a and ③b

NOTE: Use Worksheets 3a and 3b for this activity.

ACTIVITY
Pairwork: speaking

AIM
To ask and answer questions about friends.

GRAMMAR AND FUNCTIONS
Giving personal information
Questions without a question word
Negatives
Short answers

VOCABULARY
Personal information

PREPARATION
Make one copy of Worksheets 3a and 3b for each pair of students.

TIME
20 minutes

PROCEDURE
1 Draw three heads on the board, numbered 1 to 3, and write the name of a real friend of yours next to each one. In random order, write the following information about each friend around the heads without indicating which piece of information goes with which friend: job, age, surname, where they are from and whether they are married or single.
   For example:

First name: 1) _Pete_   2) _Corrine_   3) _Simon_

Job	_____	_____	_____
Age	_____	_____	_____
Surname	_____	_____	_____
Where from?	_____	_____	_____
Married?	_____	_____	_____

2 Tell the students that these are real friends of yours and that they are going to fill in the details under each head by asking you questions. They must only ask questions requiring the answer yes or no. They must complete the information about person number 1 before going on to person number 2.
   For example: 1 – Pete
   Student: *Is Pete a doctor?*
   Teacher: *Yes, he is.* (Write *doctor* in the space provided under Pete's head.)
   Student: *Is he 45?*
   Teacher: *No, he isn't.*
   Student: *Is he 36?*
   Teacher: *Yes, he is.* (Write *36* in the space provided under Pete's head.)

3 Continue answering the students' questions until you have filled in all the details about person number 1.

4 Repeat the procedure to complete information about person number 2. The students will be able to give you the information about person number 3 without asking questions. The students can then ask you other questions about your friends if they like.

5 Now ask the students to work in pairs of Student A and Student B.

6 Give a copy of Worksheet 3a to each Student A and a copy of Worksheet 3b to each Student B.

7 Tell them to imagine that these are photos of three of their friends or relatives and ask them to put their first names in the spaces provided on their worksheet.

8 Now ask them to write the following information about each person in random order in the boxes on the worksheet, without indicating which piece of information goes with which person: job, age, surname, where they are from and whether they are married or single. They must not write the information in the spaces provided under each person yet.

9 When they have done that, ask the students to exchange worksheets and take it in turns to ask and answer questions about their partner's friends. They should write in the details about their partner's friends in the spaces provided on their partner's worksheet.

OPTION
Do the same activity using real photos of the students' friends or family.

FIRST NAME   1) _____   2) _____   3) _____

Job   _____   _____   _____

Age   _____   _____   _____

Surname   _____   _____   _____

Where from? _____   _____   _____

Married? _____   _____   _____

PHOTOCOPIABLE

Memory test **Worksheets** **4a** and **4b**

ACTIVITY
Pairwork and groupwork: speaking

AIM
To look at a picture for a short time and to memorise as many details as possible.

GRAMMAR AND FUNCTIONS
There is/are
How many ...?

VOCABULARY
Office vocabulary

PREPARATION
Make one copy of Worksheets 4a and 4b for every four students in the class.

TIME
20 minutes

PROCEDURE

1 Divide the class into Group A and Group B.

2 Ask the students to work with a partner from the same group.

3 Give a copy of Worksheet 4a to each pair of students in Group A and a copy of Worksheet 4b to each pair of students in Group B. They must not show their picture to students from the other group.

4 Explain that they are going to do a memory test by looking at the other group's picture for a short time and remembering as many details as possible. But before they do this, they are going to prepare questions for one another.

5 Ask the students to write questions about their own picture, starting *How many ...?*
For example:
   How many people are there?
   How many chairs are there?

6 When they have done that, ask each Group A pair to work with a Group B pair. Make sure they do not show their pictures to each other yet.

7 Tell the students that they will have 20 seconds to look at the other pair's picture and to memorise as many details as possible.

8 Ask students to exchange pictures and time this part of the activity for exactly 20 seconds. The students must then give the pictures back.

9 Pairs of students now take it in turns to ask and answer questions about one another's pictures. Encourage them to use the target language.

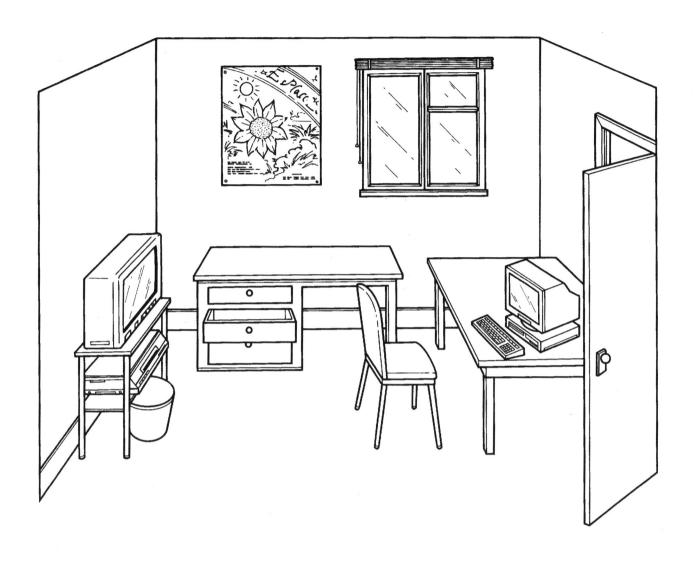

Where is it? Worksheet **5**

ACTIVITY
Whole class: speaking

AIM
To ask and say where things are.

GRAMMAR AND FUNCTIONS
Prepositions of place: *in, on, under, near*

VOCABULARY
Personal possessions

PREPARATION
Make one copy of the worksheet for each student in the class. Put a tick next to a different object at the bottom of each worksheet.

TIME
15 minutes

PROCEDURE
1   If there are more than 12 students in the class, divide them into groups.

2   Give one copy of the worksheet to each student in the class. Make sure that each student in the same group has a different object ticked on their worksheet.

3   Make sure the students know how to say all the objects in the boxes at the bottom of the worksheet.

4   Tell them that the objects are lost in the self-study room and they are going to find out where they are.

5   Before they do this, ask the students to look at the picture on their worksheet and tell you where the computer and bin are.

For example:
  Teacher: *Where's the computer?*
  Student: *Near the door./Next to the door.*
  Teacher: *Where's the bin?*
  Student: *Under the video.*

6   Tell the students that they are the only ones who know where their ticked object is in the self-study room. Ask them to draw it on their worksheet without telling the other students in the class or group where it is or what it is. Make sure each student knows how to say where their own object is.

7   Now ask the students to go round the class or group and find out where the other objects are by asking and answering questions. They must not show their own worksheet to the other students. If a student doesn't know where an object is, they should answer *I don't know.* When their partner tells them where an object is, they should draw it on their own picture. If students have problems with drawing an object, tell them to write the word for the object in the correct place instead.

Note that when the students have spoken to more than one person, they will be able to talk about the position of not only their own object, but several objects.

8   When all the students have drawn all 12 objects on their worksheet, they should sit down and compare pictures with another student. The pictures should be identical.

OPTION
You can make this activity more controlled, as follows. Cut out the cards below as indicated and give one to each student in the group. The students draw the object on their picture according to the instructions on their card and then follow the procedure as above.

There's a bag under the chair.	There are some glasses on the video recorder.	There's a mobile phone next to the computer.	There's a pen in the bin.
There are some keys on the desk.	There's a coat on the chair.	There's a camera under the table.	There's a calculator on the computer.
There's a watch next to the computer.	There's a notebook on the television.	There's a cassette player on the desk.	There are some books on the floor.

How many people ...

... have got a brother?

... have got a sister?

FIND OUT.

How many people ...

... have got some English music CDs or cassettes?

... have got an English dictionary?

FIND OUT.

How many people ...

... have got a photograph in their bag?

... have got a mobile phone in their bag?

FIND OUT.

How many people ...

... have got a comb in their bag?

... have got a diary in their bag?

FIND OUT.

How many people ...

... have got a TV in their bedroom?

... have got a computer at home?

FIND OUT.

How many people ...

... have got a Swiss watch?

... have got a Japanese camera?

FIND OUT.

How many people ...

... have got a hobby?

... have got a birthday next month?

FIND OUT.

How many people ...

... have got a bicycle?

... have got a motor bike?

FIND OUT.

How many people ...

... have got a car?

... have got a pet?

FIND OUT.

How many people ...

... have got a house near the sea?

... have got a house near the mountains?

FIND OUT.

Have you got it? Worksheet Progress check 1-5

ACTIVITY
Whole class: speaking

AIM
To find out what people in the class have got by asking and answering questions.

GRAMMAR AND FUNCTIONS
Has/have got
Have you got ...? and short answers *Yes, I have./No, I haven't.*

VOCABULARY
Personal information
Personal possessions

PREPARATION
Make one copy of the worksheet for each group of up to ten students and cut it into cards as indicated.

TIME
30 to 40 minutes

PROCEDURE

1   If there are more than ten students in the class, divide them into groups.

2   Give one card to each student in the class and tell them that they are going to find out how many people in the class or group have got the things marked on their card.

3   Write an example on the board:
    How many people have got a personal stereo?

    Ask individual students the question:
    Have you got a personal stereo?

    Encourage them to give the answer *Yes, I have* or *No, I haven't.* Each time somebody answers *Yes, I have* put a tick next to the question on the board. Leave the question and ticks on the board as you will need to refer to it later in the activity.

4   Tell the students that they are going to ask and answer similar questions beginning *Have you got ...?* and put a tick on their card next to the relevant question each time somebody answers *Yes, I have.*

5   Before they start the activity, make sure everybody knows how to ask their question. In particular, make sure that people with questions including the phrase *in their bag* or *in their bedroom* know that they must transform *their* to *your* when they ask the question.

6   Now ask the students to go round the class or group asking and answering questions and putting a tick on their card each time somebody answers *yes*.

7   When they have spoken to everybody in the class or group, ask them to work with two or three other students in their group and to write some of the information they have gathered on a poster. Before they do this, refer back to the example you wrote on the board in procedure point 3 and write a sentence reporting the information you found out.
    For example:
    Six people in the class have got a personal stereo.

    While the students are doing this, be on hand to help with language they may need.
    For example:
    Nobody in the class has got...
    Everybody in the class has got...

Photo album **Worksheet** 6

ACTIVITY
Groupwork: speaking

AIM
To talk about family relationships.

GRAMMAR AND FUNCTIONS
Possessive *'s*

VOCABULARY
Members of the family

PREPARATION
Make one copy of the worksheet for each pair or group of three students and cut the pictures out as indicated.

TIME
20 minutes

PROCEDURE
1 Ask the students to work in pairs or groups of three.

2 Give each group a copy of the worksheet cut up and ask them to take three pictures each.

3 Tell the students to imagine that these are photographs from a family photo album and that the people in the photographs are members of their family. Tell them that, in a moment, they are going to talk to their partners about them.

4 Before they do that, give them a few minutes to invent and write down some details about their imaginary relatives. Write on the board:
NAME
RELATIONSHIP TO YOU
MARRIED OR SINGLE
AGE
JOB
WHERE THEY LIVE

5 When the students have done that, ask them to take it in turns to show the pictures to their partner and explain who they are.

OPTION
If your students' English level is good enough for them to give more details about the people in the pictures, encourage them to do so. For example, have they got children, pets, a hobby, etc?

fold

When?	**What?**
YOU	

A MEMBER OF
YOUR FAMILY

My ....

When and what? Worksheet ⑦

ACTIVITY
Pairwork: writing and speaking

AIM
To ask and answer questions about daily routines.

GRAMMAR AND FUNCTIONS
Present simple for routines
Prepositions of time

VOCABULARY
Routine activities

PREPARATION
Make one copy of the worksheet for each student in the class.

TIME
20 minutes

PROCEDURE
1   Write a time of day on the board.
    For example:
        At 7.15 in the morning

    Ask the students to guess what you do every day at this time.
    For example:
        Student 1:   *You get up.*
        Teacher: *No, I don't.*
        Student 2:   *You have a shower.*
        Teacher: *No, I don't.*
        Student 3:   *You have breakfast.*
        Teacher: *Yes, that's right.*

    Now complete the example sentence on the board:
        At 7.15 in the morning I have breakfast.

    Explain that this is something you do every day – it's a routine activity. If necessary, give another example using a different preposition of time.
    For example:
        Between 6 and 7 in the evening I go to the gym.

2   Now ask the students to write similar sentences about their own daily routine in the section of their worksheet marked YOU, and about the daily routine of a member of their family in the section marked A MEMBER OF YOUR FAMILY. Ask them to write who the member of their family is in the space provided.

    Make sure they write the time under the heading *When?* and the activity under the heading *What?* They must not let the other students in the class see what they are writing. Encourage them to use a variety of prepositions of time.

3   When they have finished, ask them to fold their worksheet as indicated.

4   Now ask the students to work in pairs.

5   Tell them to hold their worksheets up so that the column marked *When?* is facing their partner and the column marked *What?* is hidden from their partner.

6   Now ask them to take it in turns to read their partner's time of day and guess what they do at this time. Repeat the activity, trying to guess what a member of their family does.

7   When they have finished, ask them to repeat the activity with a different partner.

OPTION
Give a new copy of the worksheet to each student in the class and ask them to fill it in with details about their weekend routine.

Picture 1A

Picture 2A

PHOTOCOPIABLE

Spot the similarities Worksheets  8a and 8b

NOTE: Use Worksheets 8a and 8b for this activity.

ACTIVITY
Pairwork: speaking, writing

AIM
To find similarities between two different pictures by asking and answering questions. To write brief descriptions of the pictures.

GRAMMAR AND FUNCTIONS
Describing rooms
There is/are
Is there ...?/Are there ...?
Some and *any*

VOCABULARY
Rooms and furniture

PREPARATION
Make one copy of Worksheets 8a and 8b for each pair of students in the class and cut the pictures out.

TIME
30 minutes

PROCEDURE
1 Ask the students to work in pairs of Student A and Student B. They should sit facing one another.

2 Give a copy of Worksheet 8a picture 1A to each Student A and a copy of Worksheet 8b picture 1B to each Student B.

3 Tell the students that their partner's picture is similar but not identical to their own picture.

4 Explain that they are going to try to find similarities in their pictures by describing them, not showing them to one another.

5 Elicit the language they will need to ask and answer questions about the pictures by inviting the students to ask you about a room in your home.
For example:
   Sitting room: *Are there any armchairs? Is there a television?*

6 Give the students a five-minute time limit to find as many similarities in their pictures as possible. They should keep a record of the number of similarities they find, but they do not have to remember details at this point.

7 After five minutes, stop the activity and find out which pair of students found the most similarities.

8 The students can now look at their partner's picture.

FOLLOW UP
1 Ask the students to stay in their pairs and choose the picture they like best.

2 Tell the students to look at their picture for one minute and then put it away.

3 They now have five minutes to write down as many details as they can remember about their picture. Encourage them to use the target language, including negative sentences.
For example:
   There aren't any curtains.

4 After five minutes, ask the pairs of students to give their picture and their sentences to another pair to check.

5 Repeat the activity, either now or later, using pictures 2A and 2B.

Picture 1B

Picture 2B

PHOTOCOPIABLE

9 | Habits

	You	Find someone with the same answer
What / eat for breakfast?		
Where / read the newspaper?		
When / listen to the radio?		
What / watch on televsion?		
What music / listen to?		
Where / go for holidays?		
When / go shopping?		
What time / get up on Saturdays?		
What sports / play?		
What time / go to sleep?		
When / relax?		
How / relax?		

PHOTOCOPIABLE

Habits Worksheet ❾

ACTIVITY
Whole class: writing, speaking

AIM
To write about habits and routines and to find people in the class with the same habits and routines.

GRAMMAR AND FUNCTIONS
Present simple for habits and routines
Wh- questions
How do you ...?
3rd person singular

VOCABULARY
Routine activities

PREPARATION
Make one copy of the worksheet for each student in the class.

TIME
20 to 30 minutes

PROCEDURE
1 Give a copy of the worksheet to each student in the class.

2 Ask the students to write information about themselves in the column marked *You*. Tell them it is OK to leave a space next to any activities they don't do.

3 When they have done this, ask them to go round the class asking and answering questions to find people with the same answers. Make sure they know how to ask the questions. It is important to tell the students that they must ask one another questions, not read one another's worksheets.

4 When they find someone with the same answer in their *You* column, they put that person's name in the *Find someone with the same answer* column. It is important to tell the students that they can only put the same name twice. This is to encourage them to speak to as many different partners as possible. It is a good idea to introduce the short answer *So do I* as this is a natural response to finding someone with the same answer.
For example:
　Student 1:　*What do you eat for breakfast?*
　Student 2:　*Bread and jam.*
　Student 1:　*So do I.* (Students 1 and 2 write each other's names in the space provided.)

5 When one student has found a name for each of the topics on the worksheet, stop the activity.

6 As a follow-up, ask the students to report back, orally or in written form. You may also want to use the expression *so do I* for this part of the activity.
For example:
　Petra eats bread for breakfast and so do I.
　Stefano reads the newspaper at school and so do I.

© Macmillan Publishers Limited 1997.

I like cooking... _____
_____

I don't like cooking... _____
_____

I like listening to... _____
_____

I don't like listening to... _____
_____

I like playing... _____
_____

I don't like playing... _____
_____

I like watching... _____
_____

I don't like watching... _____
_____

I like going to... _____
_____

I don't like going to... _____
_____

I like eating... _____
_____

I don't like eating... _____
_____

Sentences in a hat Worksheet **10**

ACTIVITY
Whole class: speaking

AIM
To complete unfinished sentences.
To pick sentences out of a hat and find out who wrote them by asking questions.

GRAMMAR AND FUNCTIONS
Talking about likes and dislikes

VOCABULARY
Everyday and leisure activities

PREPARATION
Make one copy of the worksheet for each group of three or four students in the class and cut it into 12 pieces as indicated. You will need a hat or a box for this activity (or two hats or boxes if there are 20 or more students in the class).

TIME
20 minutes

PROCEDURE

1 Choose two of the unfinished sentences from the worksheet, one positive and one negative, and write them on the board. Elicit possible ways of completing the sentences.
For example:
> I like cooking *cakes/at the weekend/for my friends.*
> I don't like cooking *octopus/on my birthday/for my mother-in-law.*

2 Ask the students to work in groups of three or four for the first part of this activity. Give one set of unfinished sentences to each group.

3 Ask the students to spread out the pieces of paper, face down, and to take three each.

4 Ask them to complete their three sentences in any way they like. (Refer to the examples in procedure point 1.) They should not write their names or let the students next to them see what they are writing.

5 The students now all work together as a class. Put the hat (or box) in the middle of the room. If there are 20 or more students in the class, divide them into two groups and put one hat in the middle of each group. Ask the students to fold up their completed sentences and put them in the hat.

6 Mix up the folded sentences in the hat and then tell the students that, in a moment, they are all going to stand up, take one sentence each and find out who wrote it. Demonstrate this by taking a piece of paper from the hat and reading the sentence out.
For example:
> I don't like cooking octopus.

Elicit the question they will need to ask in order to find out who wrote the sentence. Make sure they know that the question is the same whether the sentence is positive or negative:
> Do you like cooking octopus?

Ask several students the question until you find the person who wrote the sentence. Make it clear that even though someone may answer *yes* to the question, students are looking for the person who wrote it and may need to ask *Is this your sentence?*

7 Now ask the students to stand up and take one piece of paper each from the hat. If they choose their own sentence, they should put it back and take another one.

8 They are now ready to go round the class or group asking questions. All the students in the class do this simultaneously. When they find the person who wrote the sentence, they should write the person's name on the piece of paper, keep it and take another one from the hat.

9 The students repeat the activity until there are no sentences left in the hat.

10 Ask the students to return to their places and count the number of completed sentences they have collected. The student with the most sentences is the winner.

11 Ask the students to take it in turns to report back to the class or group on what they found out during the activity.
For example:
> Yuko likes cooking for her friends.
> Paolo doesn't like listening to Italian music.

Mix and match Worksheets Progress check  6-10a and 6-10b

NOTE: Use Worksheets Progress check 6–10a and 6–10b for this activity.

ACTIVITY
Groupwork: reading and speaking

AIM
To play a board game by matching verbs with other words and expressions.

GRAMMAR AND FUNCTIONS
Verb and noun collocations

VOCABULARY
Everyday activities

PREPARATION
Make one copy of Worksheet Progress check 6–10a (game board) for each group of three to five students. Make one copy of Worksheet Progress check 6–10b (cards) for each group of three to five students and cut the cards out as indicated. Provide dice and counters for each group.

TIME
30 minutes

PROCEDURE
1 Write one of the verbs from the game board on the board. For example:

   have

   Ask the students to think of words or expressions that go with *have*.
   For example:

   a bath, a drink, dinner

   Tell the students that they are going to play a game where they match verbs and other words in this way.

2 Ask the students to work in groups of three to five.

3 Give one game board and one set of cards, counters and dice to each group.

4 Before the students start playing the game, explain how to play, using the instructions below.

   If you want to make the game more challenging, instead of asking the students to simply read out an expression (see *HOW TO PLAY THE GAME* instruction 5), ask them to make a correct sentence using the expression.

5 Now the students are ready to play the game. While they are playing, go round to each group and check they are playing correctly. Be on hand to answer questions and offer help.

HOW TO PLAY THE GAME

1 Put the game board in the middle of the table.

2 Each player takes six cards. Place the rest of the cards face down in a pile on the table.

3 All the players put their counters on the square marked START and throw the dice. The first player to throw a six starts the game.

4 Player A throws the dice and moves their counter along the board according to the number on the dice.

5 Player A reads the verb on the square the counter lands on and matches it with a word or expression on one of their cards and reads out the whole expression. If the group thinks it is correct, Player A puts the card to the bottom of the pile on the table and it is Player B's turn to play.

If Player A hasn't got a word or expression that goes with the verb, they pick up a card from the top of the pile and match it with the verb if possible.

6 Now Player B throws the dice and repeats steps 4 and 5 above.

7 The game continues until the first player reaches the square marked FINISH or finishes all their cards.

Mix and match

Cards

a shower	a bath	lunch	dinner	breakfast
a drink	something to eat	home	school	work
music	the radio	television	football	a video
to the cinema	to the theatre	to bed	to work	running
to school	to a club	shopping	to sleep	the washing up
the housework	some work	the ironing	some sport	the guitar
football	music	basketball	a newspaper	a novel
a magazine	the train	the bus	home	a sauna

PHOTOCOPIABLE

Student A

PARTNER'S NAME _____	TRUE	FALSE	✔ = I'm right ✗ = I'm wrong
usually wears jeans at the weekend			
always goes to bed before midnight			
eats chocolate every day			
always remembers birthdays			
usually goes out on Saturday nights			
often does the ironing			
always gets the bus to work/school			
sometimes goes out for lunch on Sundays			
often listens to classical music			
always arrives on time for appointments			

Student B

PARTNER'S NAME _____	TRUE	FALSE	✔ = I'm right ✗ = I'm wrong
often wears trainers			
sometimes sings in the bath			
drinks coffee every day			
often writes letters to friends			
sometimes goes shopping in the evening			
usually does the washing up			
always goes to work/school by car			
usually does some sport at the weekend			
reads a newspaper every day			
often goes to the cinema			

Daily routine Worksheet **11**

ACTIVITY
Pairwork: speaking

AIM
To predict a partner's daily routine and to find out how many predictions were right.

GRAMMAR AND FUNCTIONS
Present simple: asking how often people do things
Short answers
Adverbs of frequency

VOCABULARY
Everyday actions

PREPARATION
Make one copy of the worksheet for each pair of students and cut it out as indicated.

TIME
20 minutes

PROCEDURE

1 Ask the students to work in pairs of Student A and Student B.

2 Give a copy of the top chart to each Student A and a copy of the bottom chart to each Student B.

3 Ask the students to write their partner's name in the space provided on their worksheet.

4 If the class already know one another, explain to the students that they are going to find out how well they know their partner. If this is a new class, explain that they are going to find out how good they are at guessing.

5 Ask the students to put a tick in the TRUE column if they think the information in the sentences is true for their partner or a tick in the FALSE column if they don't think it is true. They must not ask their partner yet.

6 When they have done that, the students should take it in turns to check whether their predictions were right. Make sure they know the correct question form:

    Student A: *Do you usually wear jeans at the*
              weekend?
    Student B: *Yes, I do. Do you often wear trainers?*
    Student A: *No, I don't.*

The students should put a tick or a cross in the end column next to each question, depending on whether they have guessed correctly or not.

7 When the students have finished checking their predictions with their partner, they should add up their total number of right guesses and compare scores.

12 Travel

QUESTIONNAIRE A

1   BY / YOU / OFTEN / DO / PLANE / TRAVEL / ?

2   USUALLY / YOU / DO / DO / WHAT / THE / AIRPORT / AT / ?

3   SEAT / DO / SEAT / AN / YOU / A / WINDOW / PREFER, / WHICH / OR / AISLE / ?

4   AIRLINE / YOU / FOOD / DO / LIKE / ?

5   LIKE / TO / WOULD / YOU / FLIGHT / ATTENDANT / A / BE / ?

ANSWERS

	You	Your partner
1		
2		
3		
4		
5		

QUESTIONNAIRE B

1   BY / YOU / CAR / TRAVELLING / DO / LIKE / ?

2   FAVOURITE / YOUR / WHAT'S / CAR / ?

3   YOU / GOOD / PASSENGER / A / ARE / ?

4   LIKE / MOTORWAY / DO / FOOD / YOU / ?

5   LISTEN / YOU / TO / MUSIC / YOUR / IN / CAR / USUALLY / DO / ?

ANSWERS

	You	Your partner
1		
2		
3		
4		
5		

Travel Worksheet 12

ACTIVITY
Pairwork: writing, speaking

AIM
To put words in the correct order to form questions. To ask and answer questions about travelling.

GRAMMAR AND FUNCTIONS
Present simple questions
Talking about travel

VOCABULARY
Different means of transport

PREPARATION
Make one copy of the worksheet for each pair of students in the class and cut it in half as indicated.

TIME
30 minutes

PROCEDURE

1 Divide the students into Group A and Group B.

2 Give a copy of questionnaire A to each student in Group A and a copy of questionnaire B to each student in Group B.

3 Ask the students to work with two or three other students from the same group. They should put the words of the five questions on their worksheets into the correct order and write them down. All the students should write the questions down on their own worksheet.

The correct questions are:

A 1 *Do you often travel by plane?*
   2 *What do you usually do at the airport?*
   3 *Which do you prefer, a window seat or an aisle seat?*
     (OR   *Which seat do you prefer, a window or an aisle seat?*)
   4 *Do you like airline food?*
   5 *Would you like to be a flight attendant?*
B 1 *Do you like travelling by car?*
   2 *What's your favourite car?*
   3 *Are you a good passenger?*
   4 *Do you like motorway food?*
   5 *Do you usually listen to music in your car?*

4 When the students have done that, ask them to write answers to their own questions individually on their own worksheet in the column marked *You*. Go round and check that the students have written the questions correctly and understand them.

5 Now ask them to work with a partner from the other group (ie a student from Group A should work with a student from Group B).

6 Ask the students to take it in turns to ask their partner the questions on their worksheet and to write down their partner's answers in the column marked *Your partner*. Encourage them to ask for further details from their partner by asking the additional question *Why?* or *Why not?* where appropriate. They do not have to write down the additional information.

7 When they have finished, ask the students to report back to the class about anything surprising they have found out.

Can you make a cake? Worksheet **13**

ACTIVITY
Whole class: speaking
Mill drill (For detailed instructions and advice on using mill drills, see the notes for teachers at the beginning of the Resource Pack.)

AIM
To speak to as many partners as possible, asking and answering questions about abilities.

GRAMMAR AND FUNCTIONS
Can you ...?
Yes, I can./No, I can't.

VOCABULARY
Everyday and leisure activities

PREPARATION
Make one copy of the worksheet for each group of up to 12 students. Cut the worksheet up into cards as indicated. You will need to keep one card for yourself to demonstrate the activity.

TIME
15 minutes

PROCEDURE
1 If there are more than 12 students in the class, divide them into groups. Give one picture card to each student in the class. Keep one for yourself.

2 Tell the students that they are going to ask and answer questions using the pictures on their cards as prompts. Write an example dialogue on the board, indicating the language the students should use.
   For example:
   Student A: *Can you make a cake?*
   Student B: *No, I can't. Can you play the piano?*
   Student A: *Yes, I can.*

3 Demonstrate the activity with individual students, using the card you kept for yourself. Tell the students to hold their cards so that the side with the picture on is facing them. Students ask the questions using their picture cards as prompts and answer the questions honestly.

4 Ask several pairs of students to demonstrate the activity to the whole class, using their cards as prompts and taking it in turns to ask and answer questions.

5 Now ask the students to go round the class or group asking and answering questions with as many different partners as possible, using their picture cards as prompts. In this part of the activity, the students repeat the same question several times but practise different answers each time they change partner.

6 When the students have spoken to several different partners, ask them to exchange cards and go round the class again, this time holding their cards the other way round so the picture is facing their partner. The students take it in turns to ask questions using the pictures on their partners' cards as prompts. In this part of the activity, the students ask a different question each time they change partner.

OPTION
In procedure point 2 above, it is a good idea to introduce the natural responses *So can I / I can't / Neither can I / I can* and to extend the sample dialogue.
   For example:
   Student A: *Can you make a cake?*
   Student B: *Yes, I can.*
   Student A: *So can I. / I can't!*
   Student B: *Can you play the guitar?*
   Student A: *No, I can't.*
   Student B: *Neither can I. / I can!*

Student A

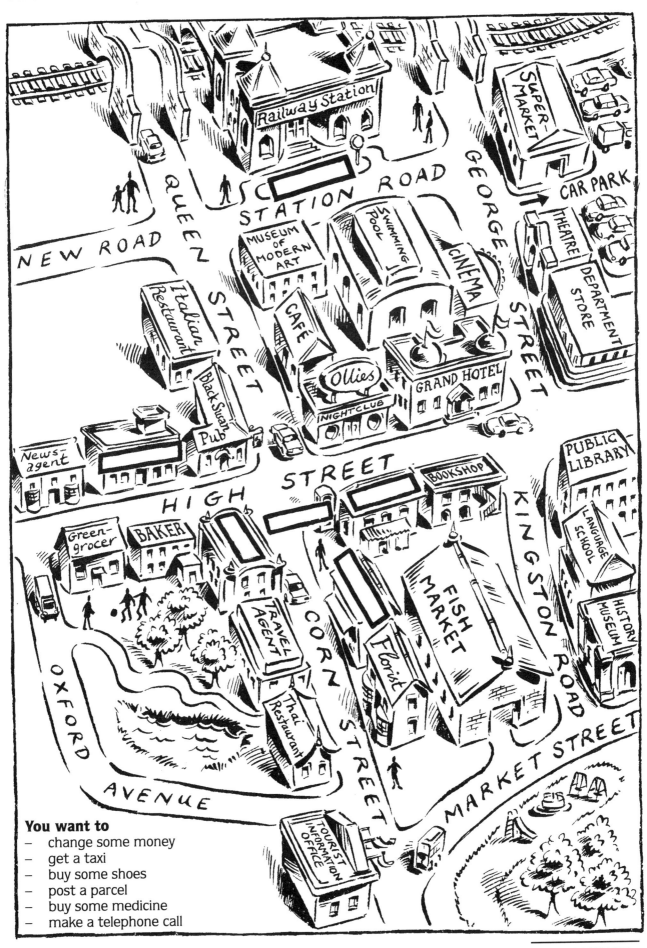

You want to

- change some money
- get a taxi
- buy some shoes
- post a parcel
- buy some medicine
- make a telephone call

Where can I buy some bread? Worksheets  14a and 14b

NOTE: Use Worksheets 14a and 14b for this activity.

ACTIVITY
Pairwork: speaking

AIM
To ask and say where places are.

GRAMMAR AND FUNCTIONS
Where can I ...?
There's a ...
Prepositions of place
Asking for and giving directions

VOCABULARY
Shops and town facilities

PREPARATION
Make one copy of Worksheet 14a and one copy of Worksheet 14b for each pair of students in the class.

TIME
20 minutes

PROCEDURE
1   Ask the students to work in pairs of Student A and Student B.

2   Explain that you are going to give them a plan of the centre of a town. Point out that there are some names of places missing on their plan.

3   Give a copy of Worksheet 14a to each Student A and a copy of Worksheet 14b to each Student B. Tell them not to show their plan to their partner at any time during this activity. Explain that the places which are missing from their plan are marked on their partner's plan. They are going to ask for and give information about places on their plan and write in the names of the missing places.

4   Before they start the activity, ask the students to look at their plan and to give you some information.
    For example, ask the question:
    Where can I have a cup of tea?

    Elicit the answer:
    There's a café in Queen Street, opposite the Italian Restaurant / between the Museum of Modern Art and Ollie's Nightclub.

Ask another question:
    Where can I see a film?

Elicit the answer:
    There's a cinema in George Street, near the Grand Hotel.

Write an example dialogue on the board.

5   Point out the list of things the students need to ask for (on their worksheets).

6   Ask the students to work with their partner and to take it in turns to ask for the information they need and to answer their partner's questions. They should ask and answer questions as in the example dialogue on the board. Each time they find a place on their plan according to their partner's instructions, they should write in the name.

7   When they have finished, they should compare plans, which should be identical.

OPTION
Instead of asking the students to ask and say where places are, ask them to give directions for how to get to the places. Tell the students that they are at the Tourist Information Office. They should ask for and give directions for the places they need to find.
    For example:
    Student A: *Is there a bank near here?*
    Student B: *Yes, there is. Go up Corn Street and it's on the left, next to the travel agent's.*
    Student A: *Oh yes, thank you. (Student A writes the name of the place on their plan.)*
    Student B: *Is there a baker's near here?*
    Student A: *Yes, there is. Go along Oxford Avenue, turn right and it's on the right, between the greengrocer's and the bank.*
    Student B: *Oh yes, thank you. (Student B writes the name of the place on their plan.)*

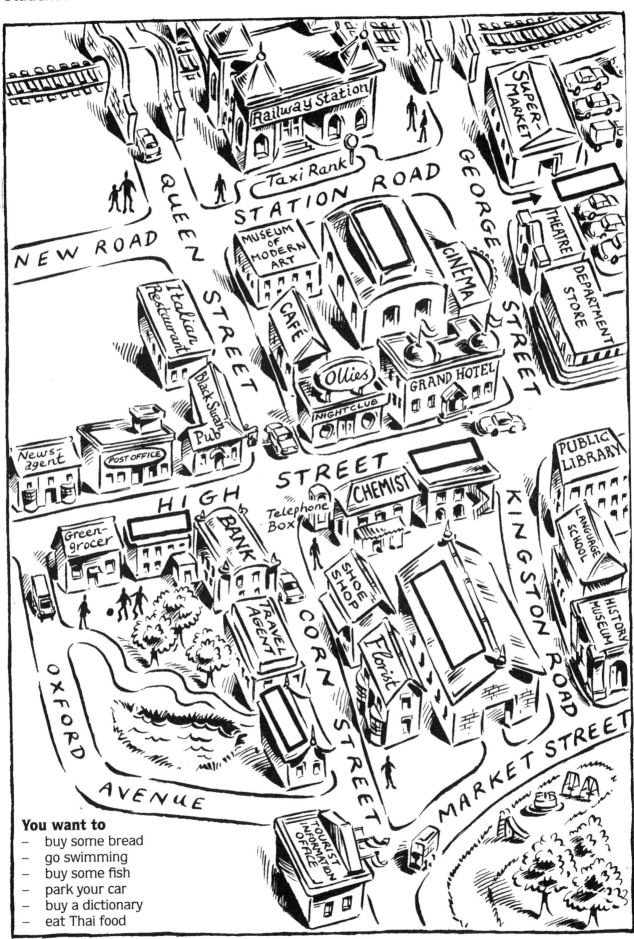

You want to
– buy some bread
– go swimming
– buy some fish
– park your car
– buy a dictionary
– eat Thai food

You are watching a horror film.

You are drinking a very hot cup of tea.

You are running to catch a bus.

You are writing a romantic letter.

You are looking in the mirror.

You are buying some flowers.

You are speaking in public.

You are looking at paintings in an art gallery.

You are eating something you don't like.

You are reading a sad story.

You are making a sandwich.

You are doing the ironing.

You are having a sauna.

You are watching a funny film.

You are taking an exam.

You are waiting to see the dentist.

You are standing in a crowded bus.

You are riding a bicycle up a hill.

You are learning to drive.

You are singing an opera.

What am I doing? **Worksheet** 15

ACTIVITY
Whole class: speaking

AIM
To mime an activity for the rest of the class to guess.

GRAMMAR AND FUNCTIONS
Present continuous

VOCABULARY
Everyday and leisure activities

PREPARATION
Make one copy of the worksheet for each team of five to eight students and cut it up into mime cards as indicated.

TIME
30 minutes

PROCEDURE
1 Ask the students to watch you and guess what you are doing. Mime something simple like eating a pizza. You do not have to be a brilliant mime artist, but it is essential that you are willing to mime enthusiastically and not be embarrassed – this will put the students at ease when it is their turn to do a mime. While you are miming, encourage the students to call out guesses as soon as they have an idea. Make sure they are using the present continuous. If necessary, mime another activity, for example making a cup of tea.

2 Tell the students that they are going to take it in turns to mime an activity for the other students to guess. Before they begin, divide them into teams of five to eight.

3 Decide which team is going to play first and ask them to choose a student to do the first mime.

4 Give the first player a mime card and explain to the class that, while he/she is miming the activity, only the members of his/her team are allowed to call out guesses. If his/her team do not guess the activity correctly, the other teams are allowed to guess. Teams score two points for a correct guess.

5 Continue until all the mime cards have been used. The team with the highest score are the winners.

OPTION
If you think your students may be embarrassed to mime in front of the whole class, or if you have a very large class, make one copy of the worksheet for each group of five to eight students and ask them to do the activity in their groups.

Picture A

Spot the differences   **Worksheets Progress check**  **and**

NOTE: Use Worksheets Progress check 11–15a and 11–15b for this activity.

ACTIVITY
Pairwork: speaking

AIM
To find ten differences between two pictures by asking and answering questions.

GRAMMAR AND FUNCTIONS
There is/are
Is/Are there ...?
How many ...?
Some and *any*
Prepositions of place
Present continuous
The article

VOCABULARY
General

PREPARATION
Make one copy of Worksheets Progress check 11-15a and 11-15b for each pair of students in the class.

TIME
20 minutes

PROCEDURE
1 Ask the students to work in pairs of Student A and Student B. They should sit facing one another.

2 Give a copy of Worksheet Progress check 11-15a to each Student A and a copy of Worksheet Progress check 11-15b to each Student B. Tell the students not to show their picture to their partner.

3 Tell the students that their partner's picture is almost identical to their own picture, but that there are ten differences.

4 Explain that they are going to try to find the ten differences by describing their pictures and asking and answering their partner's questions, not showing their pictures to one another.

5 When they have finished, check their answers. The differences are as follows:

PICTURE A
1 There's a florist's between the greengrocer's and the travel agent's.
2 The man coming out of the greengrocer's is carrying a shopping basket.
3 The woman outside the café is playing a guitar.
4 There's a dog next to the woman.
5 The bus is almost empty.
6 The motorbike has no passenger.
7 The person riding the bicycle is wearing a helmet.
8 The two people sitting at a table in front of the café are eating sandwiches.
9 The other person sitting at a table in front of the café is doing a crossword.
10 A man is taking a photograph of two children eating ice cream.

PICTURE B
1 There's a newsagent's between the greengrocer's and the travel agent's.
2 The man coming out of the greengrocer's is carrying some flowers.
3 The woman outside the café is playing a violin.
4 There's no dog next to the woman.
5 The bus is very crowded.
6 There are two people on the motorbike.
7 The person riding the bicycle is not wearing a helmet.
8 The two people sitting at a table in front of the café are drinking tea.
9 The other person sitting at a table in front of the café is writing postcards.
10 A man is taking a photograph of two children eating hamburgers.

OPTION
Ask the students to stay in their pairs and to look at Worksheet Progress check 11-15a for one minute. Then ask them to put the picture away and write down as many details as they can remember about the picture. After five minutes, ask the pairs of students to give their sentences to another pair to check.

Picture B

Reward Elementary
Resource Pack

fold ✂ fold

WEATHER?

HOTEL?

FLIGHT?

PEOPLE?

FOOD?

BEACH?

NIGHTLIFE?

ENTERTAINMENT?

SCENERY?

TOWN?

PHOTOCOPIABLE

How was your holiday? Worksheet 16

ACTIVITY
Whole class: speaking

Mill drill (For detailed instructions and advice on using mill drills, see the notes for teachers at the beginning of the Resource Pack.)

AIM
To speak to as many partners as possible, asking and answering questions about a holiday.

GRAMMAR AND FUNCTIONS
Was/were
What was it like?

VOCABULARY
Words associated with holidays

PREPARATION
Make one copy of the worksheet for each group of up to ten students. Cut the worksheet up into cards, being careful to cut and fold as indicated. You will need to keep one card for yourself to demonstrate the activity.

TIME
15 minutes

PROCEDURE
1   If there are more than ten students in the class, divide them into groups. Give one folded card to each student in the class. Keep one for yourself.

2   Tell the students that they are going to ask and answer questions about a holiday using their cards as prompts, but, before they do this, ask them to look at the picture on their card and think of an adjective or adjectives to describe it. They should write the adjective or adjectives in the space provided under the picture. Be on hand to help the students and make sure they write appropriate adjectives for their pictures.
For example:

weather:	*very warm/hot and sunny*
hotel:	*big and modern/nice and clean*

flight:	*very comfortable/fine*
people:	*very friendly*
food:	*delicious/very good*
beach:	*lovely and clean/nice and quiet*
nightlife:	*very lively/good fun*
entertainment:	*very good/OK*
scenery:	*lovely/beautiful*
town:	*very pretty/nice and quiet*

3   Now write an example dialogue on the board, indicating the language the students should use.
For example:

Student A: *How was your holiday?*
Student B: *It was great.*
Student A: *What was the weather like?*
Student B: *It was hot and sunny.*

4   Demonstrate the activity with individual students, using the card you kept for yourself. Tell the students to hold their cards so that the picture is facing them and the question prompt is facing their partner. Ask several pairs of students to demonstrate the activity to the whole class, using the cards as prompts.

5   Now ask the students to go round the class or group and ask and answer questions with as many different partners as possible, using their cards as prompts. In this part of the activity, the students ask a different question, but give the same answer each time they change partner.

6   When the students have finished, ask them to exchange cards and to go round the class or group again, this time holding their cards the other way round so that the question prompt is facing them, and the picture is facing their partner. The students take it in turns to ask and answer questions using the cards as prompts. In this part of the activity, the students ask the same question, but give a different answer each time they change partner.

7   The students continue asking and answering in this way until they have spoken to as many different partners as possible.

On an average day, how many people ...
... eat some fresh fruit?
... eat some green vegetables?

FIND OUT.

On an average day, how many people ...
... eat some brown bread?
... drink some beer or wine?

FIND OUT.

On an average day, how many people ...
... put some sugar in tea or coffee?
... eat some chips?

FIND OUT.

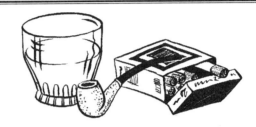

On an average day, how many people ...
... smoke some cigarettes or a pipe?
... drink some milk?

FIND OUT.

On an average day, how many people ...
... take some medicine?
... do some exercise?

FIND OUT.

On an average day, how many people ...
... take some vitamin pills?
... play a sport?

FIND OUT.

On an average day, how many people ...
... eat some pasta?
... eat some red meat?

FIND OUT.

On an average day, how many people ...
... eat a burger?
... eat a pizza?

FIND OUT.

Health survey **Worksheet** **17a**

NOTE: This activity is not linked to the activity on Worksheet 17b.

ACTIVITY
Whole class: speaking

AIM
To do a health survey.

GRAMMAR AND FUNCTIONS
Countable and uncountable nouns
Some and *any*

VOCABULARY
Food and drink

PREPARATION
Make one copy of the worksheet for each group of up to eight students and cut it up into cards as indicated.

TIME
30 minutes

PROCEDURE
1 If there are more than eight students in the class, divide them into groups.

2 Give one card to each student in the class and tell them that they are going to find out some information about the health of their group.

3 Write an example on the board:
> *On an average day, how many people eat some eggs?*

Elicit the question they will need to ask individual students in order to find out the answer to this question:
> *On an average day, do you eat any eggs?*

Write another example on the board:
> *On an average day, do you walk two kilometres or more?*

4 Tell the students that they are going to ask and answer similar questions in order to answer the questions on their cards. They should put a tick next to the relevant question on their card each time somebody answers *Yes, I do* and a cross each time somebody answers *No, I don't.*

5 Before they start the activity, make sure everybody knows how to ask their question. In particular, make sure they transform *some* into *any* in the question form.

6 Now ask the students to go round the class or group asking and answering questions and putting a tick or cross next to the questions on their card each time they change partner.

7 When they have spoken to everybody in the class or group, ask them to work with two or three other students in their group and to write some of the information they have gathered on a poster.
For example:
> *Five people in our group eat some fresh fruit on an average day.*
> *Only one person doesn't eat any green vegetables.*

OPTION
Compare the class results with the results of a survey carried out into the health habits of British people.
On an average day,
> 78% eat some fresh fruit
> 77% eat some green vegetables
> 60% eat some brown bread
> 47% drink some beer or wine
> 46% put some sugar in their tea or coffee
> 33% eat chips
> 31% smoke
> 30% drink some milk
> 30% take some medicine
> 22% do some exercise
> 16% take some vitamin pills
> 8% play a sport
> 22% eat some pasta
> 31% eat some red meat
> 38% eat a burger
> 12% eat a pizza.

Generally, women are healthier than men and young people drink more alcohol and smoke more cigarettes.

fold ✂ fold

Where / go tonight?	

What / do after this lesson?	

What / eat tonight?	

What film / watch?	

What / do this weekend?	

Where / meet this evening?	

Which CD / listen to?	

Where / go for lunch?	

What / bring to the party?	

What / have for dessert?	

What shall we do? **Worksheet** 17b

NOTE: This activity is not linked to the activity on Worksheet 17a.

ACTIVITY
Whole class: writing, speaking
Mill drill (For detailed instructions and advice on using mill drills, see the notes for teachers at the beginning of the Resource Pack.)

AIM
To speak to as many partners as possible, asking for and making suggestions.

GRAMMAR AND FUNCTIONS
Asking for and making suggestions

VOCABULARY
Leisure activities

PREPARATION
Make one copy of the worksheet for each group of up to ten students. Cut the worksheet up into cards, being careful to cut and fold as indicated. You will need to keep one card for yourself to demonstrate the activity.

TIME
20 minutes

PROCEDURE

1   If there are more than ten students in the class, divide them into groups. Give one folded card to each student in the class. Keep one for yourself.

2   Ask the students to think of a suggestion for the question on their card and to write it in the space provided.
For example:
   Where/go tonight?
   Suggestion: *go to the cinema*
   What/do after this lesson?
   Suggestion: *play tennis*

3   When the students have done that, ask them to fold their card so that the question is on one side and the suggestion is on the other side.

4   Tell the students that they are going to ask for and make suggestions, using the cards as prompts. Write an example dialogue on the board indicating the language the students should use.
For example:
   Student A: *Where shall we go tonight?*
   Student B: *Let's go to the cinema.*

5   Demonstrate the activity with individual students. Tell the students to hold their cards so that the question is facing them and the suggestion on the other side is facing their partner. Ask several pairs of students to demonstrate the activity to the whole class, using their cards as prompts.

6   Now ask the students to go round the class or group asking for and making suggestions with as many different partners as possible, using their cards as prompts. In this part of the activity, the students repeat the same question several times, but make different suggestions each time they change partner.

7   When the students have finished, ask them to exchange cards and to go round the class or group again, this time holding their cards the other way round so the question is facing their partner. The students take it in turns to ask for and make suggestions, using their cards as prompts. In this part of the activity, the students ask a different question each time they change partner, but repeat the same suggestion several times.

8   The students continue asking for and making suggestions in this way until they have spoken to as many different partners as possible.

Fabio was from Rome in Italy.	Last summer, he studied English in Oxford.	He had a lot of friends in Oxford,
but he really wanted an English girlfriend.	Fabio had a problem. He wanted to be big and strong,	but he was small and very thin.
One night he decided to go to a nightclub. At the club, he watched the people dancing	and then he noticed a nice young woman.	To his surprise, she smiled at him, walked across the room and asked him to dance.
Fabio loved dancing, but after three records, he fainted.	His friends carried him outside and were surprised to find	that he had six pullovers on under his jacket.

Poor Fabio Worksheet 18

ACTIVITY
Groupwork: speaking, reading

AIM
To predict a story from pictures and to match lines of a story to pictures.

GRAMMAR AND FUNCTIONS
Past simple: regular verbs

VOCABULARY
General

PREPARATION
Make one copy of the worksheet for each group of three students and cut it up as indicated.

TIME
30 to 40 minutes

PROCEDURE
1   Ask the students to work in groups of three.

2   Give each group a copy of the picture story but do not give them the text yet. Explain that they are going to read the story, but that before they do that, they should spend a few minutes in their groups looking at the picture story and trying to work out what is happening.

3   Now write the following verbs on the board. Ask the students to work in their groups and to decide which verbs they expect to see in the story. You may need to explain the meaning of some of them.

work   be   play   decide   receive   marry
smile   dance   study   watch   ask   die
want   walk   have   carry   open   finish
faint   notice

4   When the students have done that, work with the whole class and ask groups of students to take it in turns to call out the verbs they have chosen. Underline the verbs they call out and do not worry about whether they appear in the text of the story or not at this stage.

5   Elicit the past tense of the verbs you have underlined and pre-teach other words or expressions from the story if necessary.

6   Now the students are ready to read the story. Give each group a copy of the cut-up text and ask them to match one piece of text to each picture.

7   Check that they have put the story in the correct order and note how many verbs they had predicted correctly.

OPTION
Ask the students to work in their groups and to put the verbs from the story into three columns according to the pronunciation of the *-ed* endings:

/d/	/id/	/t/
studied	wanted	watched
carried	decided	walked
loved	fainted	asked
smiled		noticed
		danced

FOLLOW-UP
1   You can use the cut-up text of the story to do a 'community dictation'.

2   Ask the students to work in groups of up to 12 and give each student one part of the story in random order.

3   Now ask them to stand up and to form a line in the order of the story by saying their sentences aloud. They will need to repeat their own sentence several times and listen to the other students' sentences carefully.

4   When the story is in the correct order, ask the students to sit down in their groups and get ready to write the story.

5   Explain that each student is going to write the whole story. Each student dictates their own sentence to the rest of the group and answers questions about the spelling and punctuation of their sentence.

6   Ask the student with the first line to read it out for the rest of the group to write down. The students then take it in turns to read out their sentences in order for the rest of the group to write down.

7   When they have finished, give out copies of the complete story so that the students can correct their own work.

Dear penfriend,

My name is _____ and I'm _____
(age)

- -
fold

I've got _____ , _____ hair and _____ eyes.

- -
fold

I'm _____ metre _____ and I'm quite _____
(size)

- -
fold

I look like my _____

- -
fold

I'm _____ and _____
(character)

- -
fold

I like _____ , _____ and

_____

- -
fold

but I don't like _____

Please write to me and tell me what you're like.

PHOTOCOPIABLE

What are you like? Worksheet **19**

ACTIVITY
Groupwork: writing

AIM
To write a description of a person.

GRAMMAR AND FUNCTIONS
Talking about appearance

VOCABULARY
Adjectives to describe people's appearance and character
Physical features

PREPARATION
Make one copy of the worksheet for each student in the class.

TIME
30 minutes

PROCEDURE
1 Introduce the idea of a penfriend and ask the students what they would write if they were writing to a penfriend for the first time.

2 Explain that the students are going to write a letter to a penfriend and that they are going to invent the details.

3 Divide the class into groups of eight and give one copy of the worksheet to each student in the group.

4 Ask the students to invent a name and an age for the person writing the letter and write it in the space provided. Now ask them to write F or M at the bottom of the page according to whether they have written the name of woman (F) or a man (M).

5 When they have done that, ask them to fold their piece of paper so that the sentence they have written is hidden, and the next sentence beginning *I've got ...* is visible. They should then give it to the student on their left.

6 Ask the students to invent details to complete the sentence which is now at the top of the piece of paper they have received, taking note of whether the person is a woman or a man.

7 When they have done that, ask them to fold it as before and give it to the student on their left.

8 Repeat the activity until all the sentences have been completed.

9 Tell the students to open out the completed letter they have received. This is their new penfriend.

10 If there are any words or phrases that the students do not understand or think are incorrect, tell them to find the student who wrote them and ask them to explain or correct the word or phrase.

OPTION
The students can use the same worksheet to write a reply to their penfriend by filling in the blanks with real details about themselves.
Alternatively, ask the students to use the same worksheet to write a description of somebody else in the class or of a famous person for the rest of the class to guess.

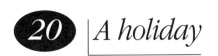

YOUR LAST HOLIDAY	YOUR PARTNER'S LAST HOLIDAY PARTNER'S NAME _____ HE/SHE WENT TO	✔ = I was right ✗ = I was wrong
I WENT TO _____	_____	
I went with… _____	He/she went with… _____	
I travelled by… _____	He/she travelled by… _____	
I stayed in a… _____	He/she stayed in a… _____	
I stayed there for… _____	He/she stayed there for… _____	
The weather was… _____	The weather was… _____	
I bought… _____	He/she bought… _____	
I visited… _____	He/she visited… _____	
I ate… _____	He/she ate… _____	
I drank… _____	He/she drank… _____	
In the evenings, I… _____	In the evenings, he/she… _____	

PHOTOCOPIABLE

A holiday Worksheet 20

ACTIVITY
Pairwork: speaking

AIM
To guess details about a partner's last holiday and to find out how many predictions were right.

GRAMMAR AND FUNCTIONS
Past simple: irregular verbs
Yes/no questions and short answers

VOCABULARY
Irregular verbs
Verbs associated with holidays

PREPARATION
Make one copy of the worksheet for each student in the class.

TIME
30 minutes

PROCEDURE
1 Give one copy of the worksheet to each student in the class.

2 Ask the students to write about their last holiday by completing the sentences in the column marked YOUR LAST HOLIDAY. Tell them not to show the other students what they are writing.

3 When they have done that, ask them to work in pairs, but tell them that it is important not to show their worksheet to their partner. They should sit facing one another.

4 Tell the students to write their partner's name in the space provided at the top of the column marked YOUR PARTNER'S LAST HOLIDAY. They then need to ask where their partner went for their last holiday and write the name of the place in the space provided under the name. They must not ask for any further information yet.

5 Now tell the students that they are going to guess what their partner did on holiday by completing the sentences in the column marked YOUR PARTNER'S LAST HOLIDAY. Emphasise again that they must not ask their partner yet.

6 When they have done that, the students should take it in turns to check whether they guessed correctly by asking their partner questions.
For example:
    Student A: *Did you go with your family?*
    Student B: *No, I didn't. I went with my friends.*
                 Did you go with your husband?
    Student A: *Yes, I did.*

The students should put a tick or a cross in the end column, depending on whether they guessed correctly or not.

If necessary, give the students time to write down the questions they need to ask before they begin this part of the activity.

7 When the students have finished checking their guesses with their partner, they should add up their total number of right guesses. Find out who scored the highest total.

FOLLOW-UP
Ask the students to write a summary of their partner's holiday.

Everybody in the class drank some fruit juice for breakfast.

TRUE OR FALSE? FIND OUT.

Everybody in the class had dinner at home yesterday.

TRUE OR FALSE? FIND OUT.

Everybody in the class ate some chocolate yesterday.

TRUE OR FALSE? FIND OUT.

Everybody in the class spent some money yesterday evening.

TRUE OR FALSE? FIND OUT.

Everybody in the class ate some meat yesterday.

TRUE OR FALSE? FIND OUT.

Everybody in the class read a newspaper yesterday.

TRUE OR FALSE? FIND OUT.

Everybody in the class bought some cigarettes yesterday.

TRUE OR FALSE? FIND OUT.

Everybody in the class went out last night.

TRUE OR FALSE? FIND OUT.

Everybody in the class visited a foreign country last year.

TRUE OR FALSE? FIND OUT.

Everybody in the class wrote some letters last weekend.

TRUE OR FALSE? FIND OUT.

Everybody in the class did some sport last week.

TRUE OR FALSE? FIND OUT.

Everybody in the class made some telephone calls yesterday.

TRUE OR FALSE? FIND OUT.

Find out   Worksheet Progress check   16-20

ACTIVITY
Whole class: speaking

AIM
To find out information about members of the class by asking and answering questions.

GRAMMAR AND FUNCTIONS
Simple past: regular and irregular verbs
Yes/no questions
Countable and uncountable nouns
Some and *any*

VOCABULARY
General

PREPARATION
Make one copy of the worksheet for each group of up to 12 students. Cut the cards out as indicated.

TIME
20 minutes

PROCEDURE

1   Write a statement about the class on the board.
For example:
> *Everybody in the class ate some vegetables yesterday.*

Find out whether this is true by asking individual students:
> *Did you eat any vegetables yesterday?*

Write a tick on the board each time somebody answers *Yes, I did* and a cross each time somebody answers *No, I didn't*. Then cross the statement out and write the correct information.
For example:
> *Seven students ate some vegetables yesterday.*
> *Nine students didn't eat any vegetables yesterday.*

Now tell the students that they are going to correct similar statements.

2   If there are more than 12 students in the class, divide them into groups. Give one card to each student in the class.

3   Tell the students that they are responsible for finding out whether the statement on their own card is true or false, and correcting it if necessary.

4   Now ask the students to go round the class or group asking and answering questions. Tell them to write down on their card a tick each time somebody answers *Yes, I did* and a cross each time somebody answers *No, I didn't*.

5   When they have finished, they should sit down and take it in turns to report back to the class or group on what they found out during the activity.

Student A

John Lennon was born in (1) 19 _____ and lived with his aunt and uncle in Liverpool.
When he was 12 he learned to play the (3) _____ but his ambition
wasn't to be a musician – he wanted to be a millionaire! He was (5) _____
years old when his mother died in a car accident.

As a teenager, he created his first group and they were called the Quarrymen. He met
(7) _____ in 1955 and they started the Beatles in 1960.
(9) _____ became their manager in 1961.

John married Cynthia in 1962 and they had a son called
(11) _____ . Later, John and Cynthia divorced and
in November 1966 John met Yoko Ono in an art gallery in London.

He met (13) _____ in 1967
and started doing meditation. In the same year, Brian Epstein died.

On March 20th 1969, John and Yoko (15) _____
and the following year John left the Beatles and created the Plastic Ono band.
They had their first hit with 'Imagine' in (17) 19 _____ .

In 1975, John and Yoko went to New York and had a son called
(19) _____ .

John Lennon was shot outside his home in New
York on December 8th 1980.

QUESTIONNAIRE

(1) _____

(3) _____

(5) _____

(7) _____

(9) _____

(11) _____

(13) _____

(15) _____

(17) _____

(19) _____

John Lennon Worksheets 21a and 21b

NOTE: Use Worksheets 21a and 21b for this activity.

ACTIVITY
Pairwork: reading, writing, speaking

AIM
To write and ask questions to obtain information in order to complete a life history.

GRAMMAR AND FUNCTIONS
Past simple
Wh- questions

VOCABULARY
Life history

PREPARATION
Make one copy of Worksheets 21a and 21b for each pair of students in the class.

TIME
50 to 60 minutes

PROCEDURE

1 Tell the students that they are going to read some information about John Lennon's life. Make sure the students know who John Lennon was and that he died some time ago. Point out that there is some information missing from the text that you are going to give them.

2 Divide the students into Group A and Group B. Give one copy of Worksheet 21a to each student in Group A and one copy of Worksheet 21b to each student in Group B.

3 Ask the students to work with a partner from the same group for the first part of the activity. Explain that there are some details missing from their text and that they should write down the questions they need to ask to obtain the missing information. All the students must write the questions down in the spaces provided on their worksheet.
For example:

Student A: (1) *When was John Lennon born?*
            (3) *What did he learn to play?*

Student B: (2) *Where did he live with his aunt and uncle?*
            (4) *What did he want to be?* or *What was his ambition?*

While the students are doing this, be on hand to answer questions and offer help.

4 When the students have finished writing questions, ask them to work with a partner from the other group. Student A and Student B should now sit facing one another and take it in turns to ask and answer questions in numerical order to find out the information missing from their own text. They should write the information in the blanks on their worksheet.

5 When they have finished exchanging information, the pairs of students compare their completed texts, which should be identical.

Student B

John Lennon was born in 1941 and lived with his aunt and uncle in
(2) _____. When he was 12 he learned to play the harmonica but his ambition
wasn't to be a musician – he wanted to be a (4) _____ ! He was
eighteen years old when his mother died in a car accident.

As a teenager, he created his first group and they were called (6) _____.
He met Paul McCartney in 1955 and they (8) _____ in
1960. Brian Epstein became their manager in 1961.

John married (10) _____ in 1962 and they had a son
called Julian. Later, John and Cynthia divorced and in November 1966
John met (12) _____ in an art gallery in London.

He met Maharishi Mahesh Yogi in 1967 and started doing meditation.
In the same year, (14) _____ died.

On March 20th 1969, John and Yoko got married and the following year John
left the Beatles and created (16) _____ .
They had their first hit with 'Imagine' in 1971.

In 1975, John and Yoko went to (18) _____
and had a son called Sean.

John Lennon was shot outside his home in
New York on
(20) _____ .

QUESTIONNAIRE

(2) _____

(4) _____

(6) _____

(8) _____

(10) _____

(12) _____

(14) _____

(16) _____

(18) _____

(20) _____

Find someone who ...	NAME
… has their birthday in the same month as you	_____
… thinks Friday the 13th is unlucky	_____
… knows the date of their parents' wedding anniversary	_____
… did something interesting yesterday evening	_____
… has the same favourite month as you	_____
… can remember when they last bought a CD or cassette	_____
… is looking forward to the year 2001	_____
… can tell you their brothers' and sisters' birthdays	_____
… can remember when they last went to the cinema	_____
… knows how many days there are in this month	_____
… knows the date of the next public holiday	_____
… can remember when they last wrote a letter	_____

Find someone who... **Worksheet** 22

ACTIVITY
Whole class: speaking

AIM
To ask and answer questions and to complete a chart.

GRAMMAR AND FUNCTIONS
Dates
Expressions of time

VOCABULARY
General

PREPARATION
Make one copy of the worksheet for each student in the class.

TIME
20 to 30 minutes

PROCEDURE

1 Give one copy of the worksheet to each student in the class.

2 Explain that they are going to transform the statements on their worksheet into questions and then go round the class asking one another the questions.

3 Ask them to work in pairs or small groups for the first part of the activity and to write down on a separate piece of paper the questions they will need to ask.

4 Check the questions – there may be several alternatives for one statement. For example, the question *Find someone who has their birthday in the same month as you* could be answered by any of the following questions:
    Is your birthday in February?
    When is your birthday?
    What month is your birthday?

5 Now the students are ready to go round the class asking one another the questions.

6 When they find someone who answers *yes* to a question, they put that person's name next to the statement in the space provided. It is very important to tell the students that they can only put the same name twice. This is to encourage them to speak to as many different partners as possible.

7 When one student has found a name for each of the statements on the worksheet, stop the activity.

8 As a follow-up, ask the students to say which statements were difficult to put a name to and which were easy.

What are their names? Worksheet 23

ACTIVITY
Groupwork: speaking

AIM
To find out people's names by describing them.

GRAMMAR AND FUNCTIONS
Describing people
Present continuous or present simple
Actions of the face, hands and body

VOCABULARY
Items of clothing

PREPARATION
Make one copy of the worksheet for each group of three or four students in the class and cut the pictures out as indicated. Make one copy of the worksheet for each student in the class and don't cut the pictures out.

TIME
20 minutes

PROCEDURE
1 Ask the students to work in groups of three or four.

2 Give each group one copy of the worksheet, cut up, and ask them to take three or four pictures each without showing them to the other students in the group. They should put the remaining pictures in a pile face down.

3 Tell them to imagine that they know the people in their pictures but that the other students in their group don't know them.

4 Now tell them that they are going to describe their friends to the other students in their group, but first they should spend a few minutes inventing names for them and writing down descriptions of them. Be on hand to answer questions and offer help for this part of the activity.

5 Now give one copy of the intact worksheet to each student in the class. Tell them not to identify their own pictures of people on the worksheet yet.

6 Students now take it in turns to describe the people in their own pictures, without showing them, so that the other students in the group can identify them on their own worksheet. They should begin like this:
   This is Katja. She's got short fair hair and she's wearing ...

   The other students in the group should listen to the complete description and then point to the picture of the person who fits that description. If they are right, they should write the name on the picture.

7 Continue like this until the students have finished describing their people. They should then invent names for the remaining people on the worksheet.

FOLLOW-UP
1 When the students have finished describing and writing in the names of people, tell them that there are six couples on their worksheets and that they should decide who they are.

2 When they have finished deciding which people go together as couples, ask them to compare their couples with another group. Tell them that there are no right answers, but they should explain why they put people together.

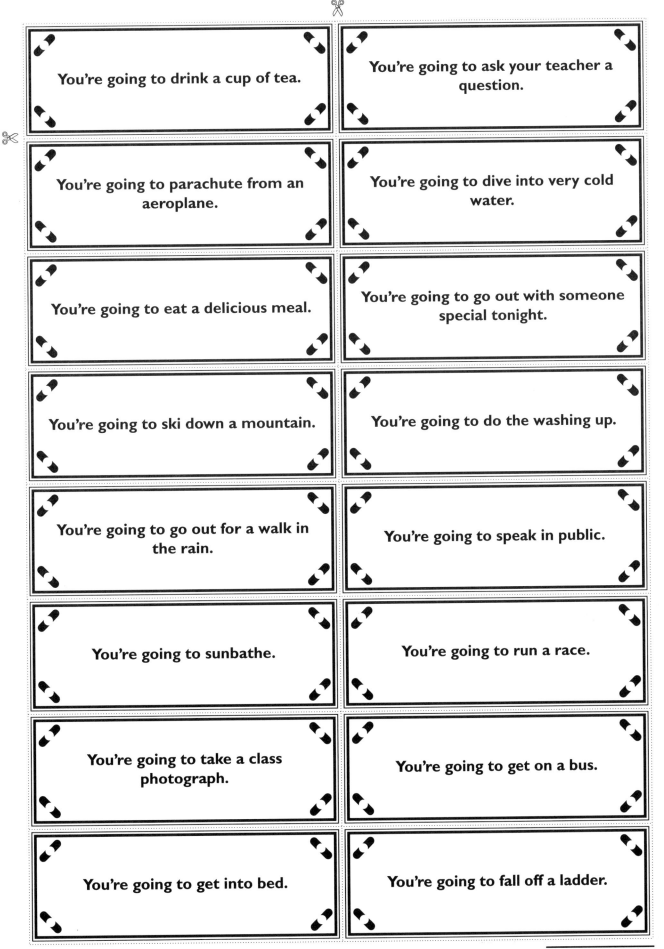

You're going to drink a cup of tea.

You're going to ask your teacher a question.

You're going to parachute from an aeroplane.

You're going to dive into very cold water.

You're going to eat a delicious meal.

You're going to go out with someone special tonight.

You're going to ski down a mountain.

You're going to do the washing up.

You're going to go out for a walk in the rain.

You're going to speak in public.

You're going to sunbathe.

You're going to run a race.

You're going to take a class photograph.

You're going to get on a bus.

You're going to get into bed.

You're going to fall off a ladder.

What am I going to do? **Worksheet**  24

ACTIVITY
Whole class: speaking

AIM
To mime the actions leading up to something you are going to do. To guess what other members of the class are going to do by watching their mime.

GRAMMAR AND FUNCTIONS
Going to + infinitive

VOCABULARY
Everyday and leisure activities

PREPARATION
Make one copy of the worksheet and cut it up into mime cards as indicated.

TIME
30 minutes

PROCEDURE

1 Ask the students to watch you. Choose one of the mime cards and mime the actions you would do in preparation for the action marked on the card (but not the action itself). Freeze just before the action itself and ask the class *What am I going to do?* You do not have to be a brilliant mime artist, but it is essential that you are willing to mime enthusiastically and not be embarrassed – this will put the students at ease when it is their turn to do a mime.

2 Tell the students that they are going to take it in turns to do similar mimes for the rest of the students to guess. But before they begin, divide the class into teams of five to eight.

3 Decide which team is going to play first and ask them to choose a student to do the first mime. Remind them they must freeze just before the action and say *What am I going to do?*

4 Give the first player a mime card and explain to the class that, when he/she freezes, only the members of his/her team are allowed to call out a guess at first. Team members should consult before guessing. If his/her team do not guess the action correctly, the other teams are allowed to guess. Teams score two points for a correct guess.

5 Continue until all the mime cards have been used. The team with the highest score are the winners.

OPTION
If you think your students may be embarrassed to mime in front of the whole class, or if you have a very large class, make one copy of the worksheet for each group of six to eight students and ask them to do the activity in their groups.

Reward Elementary
Resource Pack

fold   fold

I'd like an ice cream, please Worksheet 25

ACTIVITY
Whole class: speaking
Mill drill (For detailed instructions and advice on using mill drills, see the notes for teachers at the beginning of the Resource Pack.)

AIM
To speak to as many partners as possible, asking what people would like and making polite requests.

GRAMMAR AND FUNCTIONS
Offers and requests
Would like
Asking and saying how much things cost

VOCABULARY
Food and drink

PREPARATION
Make one copy of the worksheet for each group of up to ten students. Cut the worksheet up into cards, being careful to cut and fold as indicated. You will need to keep one card for yourself to demonstrate the activity.

TIME
15 minutes

PROCEDURE
1 As this is a controlled practice activity, it is essential that the students are familiar with the vocabulary before doing the mill drill. It is a good idea to use the pictures on the mill drill cards to revise or pre-teach the vocabulary the students will need for this activity:

Food and drink	Choice of size, flavour, etc
an ice cream	strawberry or chocolate?
some french fries	regular or large?
some water or a glass of water	sparkling or still?
some coffee or a cup of coffee	black or white?
some apple pie or a piece of apple pie	with cream or ice cream?
a burger	with fries or salad?
a Coke	regular or large?
a salad	with vinaigrette or mayonnaise?
a sandwich	(with) white or brown bread?
a steak	medium or rare?

2 If there are more than ten students in the class, divide them into groups. Give one folded picture card to each student in the class. Keep one for yourself.

3 Make sure each student knows how to say the food or drink shown in the picture on their card. In particular, make sure they know which article to use (*a*, *an* or *some*).

4 Tell the students that they are going to ask for the food or drink shown on their cards. Write an example dialogue on the board, indicating the language the students should use. For example:

    Student A: *Can I help you?*
    Student B: *I'd like an ice cream, please.*
    Student A: *Would you like strawberry or chocolate?*
    Student B: *Chocolate, please.*

5 Demonstrate the activity with individual students, using the card you kept for yourself. Tell the students to hold their cards so that the picture showing the food or drink is facing them and the picture showing the choice of size, flavour, etc is facing their partner. Ask several pairs of students to demonstrate the activity to the whole class, using their pictures as prompts.

6 Now ask the students to go round the class or group making requests and offering choices with as many different partners as possible, using their picture cards as prompts. In this part of the activity, the students request the same food or drink, but offer different sizes, flavours, etc.

7 When the students have finished, ask them to exchange cards and to go round the class or group again, this time holding their cards the other way round so that the picture showing the food or drink is facing their partner and the picture showing the choice of size, flavour, etc is facing themselves. In this part of the activity, the students ask for different food or drink each time they change partner.

8 The students continue making requests and offering choices in this way until they have spoken to as many different partners as possible.

OPTION
You can extend the dialogue so that the students practise asking and saying how much things cost. Before they start the activity, ask them to write the price of the food or drink on the part of the card showing the choice of size, flavour, etc. You can help them to decide how much these things usually cost. When all the students have done that and you have checked that they have put an appropriate price on their cards, follow the procedure as above, adding the following lines to the sample dialogue:

    Student A: *Here you are.*
    Student B: *Thank you. How much is that?*
    Student A: *That's 99p.*

Alternatively, the students can practise this three-line dialogue in a separate mill drill. Cut off the part of the cards showing the choice of size, flavour, etc and use the pictures of food and drink as mill drill cards. Ask the students to write the price of the food or drink shown on their cards on the blank side. Follow the procedure for a mill drill with students holding the cards with the pictures of food and drink facing them and the price facing their partner for the first part of the activity, and then holding the cards the other way round for the second part of the activity.

Who was the last person to eat ice cream?

FIND OUT

Who was the last person to write a letter?

FIND OUT

Who was the last person to buy some clothes?

FIND OUT

Who was the last person to give someone a present?

FIND OUT

Who was the last person to have a birthday?

FIND OUT

Who was the last person to go to the hairdresser?

FIND OUT

Who was the last person to make a new friend?

FIND OUT

Who was the last person to have a meal in a restaurant?

FIND OUT

Who was the last person to go dancing?

FIND OUT

Who was the last person to take a taxi?

FIND OUT

Who was the last person to lie on a beach?

FIND OUT

Who was the last person to do some exercise?

FIND OUT

PHOTOCOPIABLE

When did you last...? Worksheet Progress check 21-25

ACTIVITY
Whole class: speaking

AIM
To find out information about members of the class by asking and answering questions.

GRAMMAR AND FUNCTIONS
Simple past: irregular verbs
Wh- questions
Expressions of time

VOCABULARY
Everyday and leisure activities

PREPARATION
Make one copy of the worksheet for each group of up to 12 students. Cut the cards out as indicated.

TIME
15 to 20 minutes

PROCEDURE

1 If there are more than 12 students in the class, divide them into groups. Give one card to each student in the class.

2 Tell the students that they are responsible for finding the answer to the question on their own card by speaking to everybody in the class or group. Make sure each student knows how to ask their question correctly and understands that they will have to note down the times when students last did the actions in order to answer the question.
For example:
    Student A: *When did you last eat ice cream?*
    Student B: *(I ate some ice cream) last weekend.*
(Student A writes Student B's name and *last weekend*.)

    Student B: *When did you last write a letter?*
    Student A: *I wrote to my grandmother in April on her*
          birthday.
(Student B writes Student A's name and *in April*.)

3 Now ask the students to go round the class or group asking and answering questions. Tell them that they can make notes on the back of their card.

4 When they have finished, they should sit down and take it in turns to report back to the class or group on what they found out during the activity.
For example:
    Stefano was the last to eat ice cream. He ate it
      yesterday afternoon.
    Milene was the last to write a letter. She wrote to her
      sister last night.

a bottle of		a packet of	
a box of		a bar of	
a pair of		a bunch of	
a bottle of		a packet of	
a box of		a bar of	
a pair of		a bunch of	

PHOTOCOPIABLE

Snap! Worksheet 26

ACTIVITY
Pairwork: reading, speaking

AIM
To play a game of *Snap!* by making correct collocations.

GRAMMAR AND FUNCTIONS
Collocation

VOCABULARY
Items of shopping

PREPARATION
Make two copies of the worksheet for every two or three students in the class and cut the cards out as indicated.

TIME
10 to 15 minutes

PROCEDURE
1 Tell the students that they are going to play a card game called *Snap!*

2 Ask the students to work in pairs or groups of three and explain how to play the game using the instructions below.

3 The students are ready to play the game. While they are playing, go round to each group and check they are playing correctly.

HOW TO PLAY THE GAME

1 Player A shuffles the cards and deals them all out equally to all the players.

2 Players must hold their cards in a pile face down so that they can't see them.

3 Player A puts their top card face up on the table.

4 Player B puts their top card face up on top of Player A's card.

5 If the two cards go together, the first player to shout *Snap!* picks up all the cards. For example, if one card has the

words *a bottle of* and the other card has a picture of a bottle of wine or a bottle of perfume, they go together.

6 If the two cards do not go together, the next player puts a card face up on top of the pile.

7 Players continue putting down cards and shouting *Snap!* when two cards go together until they have used all their cards.

8 The player with the most cards at the end of the game is the winner.

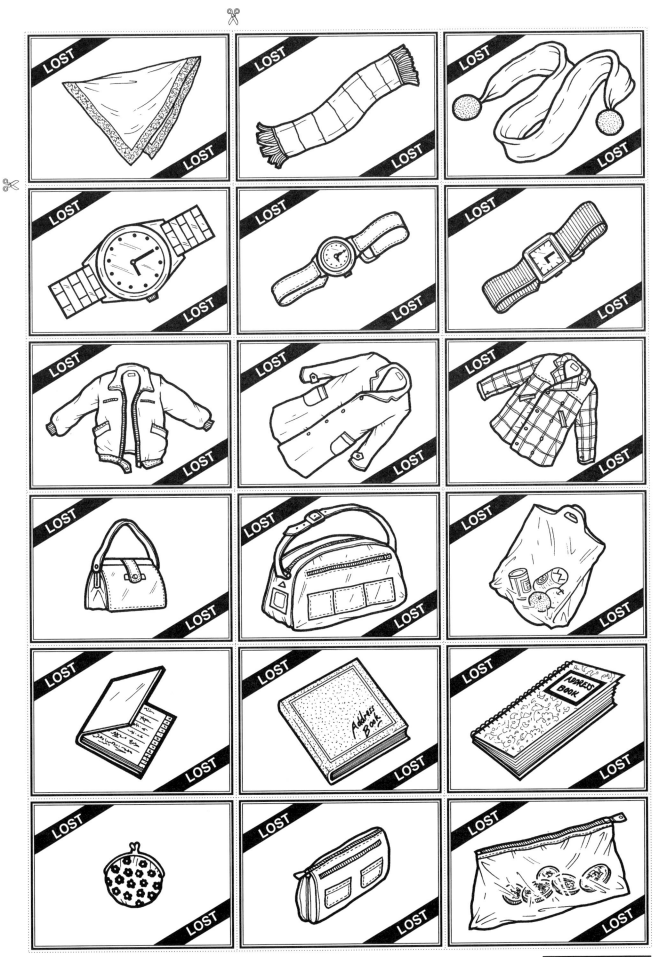

Lost and found Worksheets 27a and 27b

NOTE: Use Worksheets 27a and 27b for this activity.

ACTIVITY
Groupwork: speaking

AIM
To find lost objects by describing them.

GRAMMAR AND FUNCTIONS
Describing objects

VOCABULARY
Adjectives to describe objects
Materials

PREPARATION
Make one copy of Worksheets 27a and 27b for each group of three to five students. Cut them up into cards as indicated. Make one copy of Worksheet 27a for each group and do not cut it up.

TIME
20 minutes

PROCEDURE
1 Tell the students that you lost an object yesterday, for example a bag. Elicit the question *What's it like?* and describe it.
For example:
   It's small and made of leather.

2 Now tell the students that they are going to play a game by describing objects they have lost, using pictures as prompts.

3 Ask the students to work in groups of three to five.

4 Give one copy of the intact Worksheet 27a to each group and allow the students a few minutes to look at it. Point out that there are three different versions of each object, for example a square, silk scarf, a short wool scarf and a long wool scarf. You might want to elicit from the students words they could use to describe the other objects.
For example:
   watch: *large/small, round/square*
   jacket or coat: *short/long, (made of) leather/wool*
   bag: *small/large, (made of) leather/plastic*
   address book: *long/square, thin/thick, (made of) leather/plastic*
   purse: *small/large, round/rectangular/long, (made of) leather/plastic*

5 Now give one copy of Worksheets 27a and 27b cut up into cards to each group. Explain that for every picture card with LOST marked on it there is an identical card with FOUND marked on it. Make sure the students understand the meaning of LOST and FOUND.

6 Now ask each group of students to shuffle their LOST and FOUND cards together. Explain how to play the game using the instructions below.

7 The students are ready to play the game. While they are playing, go round to each group and check they are playing correctly.

HOW TO PLAY THE GAME

1 Each player takes six cards. They must not show their cards to the other players. Leave the rest of the cards in a pile, face down.

2 If a player has got two identical picture cards, one with LOST and one with FOUND marked on it, he/she puts them back to the bottom of the pile and takes two new cards.

3 Player A chooses one of his/her cards and tells the rest of the group, without showing his/her card, that he/she has either lost or found the object on the card. For example, if the card has got a picture of a scarf and the word LOST marked on it, Student A says *Yesterday I lost a scarf.* If the card has got a picture of a scarf and the word FOUND marked on it, Player A says *Yesterday I found a scarf.*

4 The student on Player A's left (Player B) then asks Player A to describe the object, by saying *What's it like?*

5 Player A describes the object and the other players in the group decide whether they have got a picture card showing the same object. If the description does not match another player's picture card, Player A picks up a card from the top of the pile and it is Player B's turn to play.

If another player thinks he/she has got a card showing the same object, he/she gives the card to Player A and asks *Is this it?* If the objects are the same, Player A puts the two identical picture cards back to the bottom of the pile. If the objects are not identical, Players A and B both pick up a card from the top of the pile and it is Player B's turn to play.

6 The game continues until the first player has got rid of all his/her cards. This player is the winner.

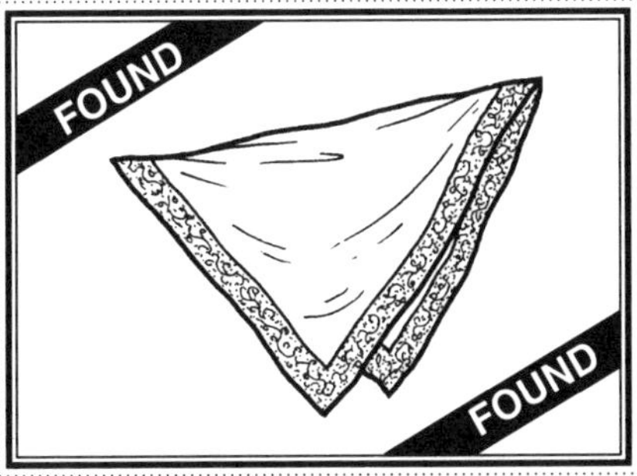
FOUND
FOUND

FOUND
FOUND

FOUND
FOUND

FOUND
FOUND

FOUND
FOUND

FOUND
FOUND

FOUND
FOUND

FOUND
FOUND

FOUND
FOUND

FOUND
FOUND

FOUND
FOUND

FOUND
FOUND

FOUND
FOUND

FOUND
Address Book
FOUND

FOUND
ADDRESS BOOK
FOUND

FOUND
FOUND

FOUND
FOUND

FOUND
FOUND

COMPLAINT	COMPLAINT	ADVICE
I feel	_____	_____
	_____	_____

COMPLAINT	COMPLAINT	ADVICE
I feel	_____	_____
	_____	_____

COMPLAINT	COMPLAINT	ADVICE
I feel	_____	_____
	_____	_____

COMPLAINT	COMPLAINT	ADVICE
My _____	**hurts**	_____
		_____

COMPLAINT	COMPLAINT	ADVICE
My _____	**hurts**	_____
		_____

COMPLAINT	COMPLAINT	ADVICE
My _____	**hurts**	_____
		_____

COMPLAINT	COMPLAINT	ADVICE
I've got	_____	_____
	_____	_____

COMPLAINT	COMPLAINT	ADVICE
I've got	_____	_____
	_____	_____

COMPLAINT	COMPLAINT	ADVICE
I've got	_____	_____
	_____	_____

PHOTOCOPIABLE

Ouch! Worksheet **28**

ACTIVITY
Pairwork, groupwork: writing, speaking

AIM
To write complaints about health and corresponding advice.
To play a game by matching advice to complaints.

GRAMMAR AND FUNCTIONS
Asking and saying how you feel:
I feel ...
My ... hurts
I've got ...
Sympathising and giving advice: *should, shouldn't*

VOCABULARY
Adjectives to describe how you feel
Nouns for illnesses

PREPARATION
Make one copy of the worksheet for each pair of students in the class but do not cut it up yet. You will need to provide scissors for each group of four students.

TIME
30 minutes

PROCEDURE
1　Write the following incomplete sentences on the board and ask the students to suggest different ways of completing them:
I feel ...
My ... hurts
I've got ...

2　Now ask the students to work in pairs.

3　Give one copy of the worksheet to each pair of students and ask them to complete the health complaints on their worksheets by writing in the spaces provided. They should not complete the advice column yet. Be on hand to answer questions and offer help for this part of the activity.

4　When the students have done that, ask them to work with another pair of students and to exchange their worksheet with them.

5　Now pairs of students should read the complaints on their new worksheet and write a relevant piece of advice, using *should* or *shouldn't*, for each complaint in the spaces provided on the worksheet.

6　When the students have done that, ask them to stay in groups of four for the rest of the activity. Ask each pair to cut their worksheet up as indicated, keeping the advice cards separate from the complaint cards. They should then combine complaint cards and advice cards in their groups. (There will be two complaint cards for every advice card.)

7　Ask them to shuffle the complaint cards and the advice cards and put them in two separate piles on the table.

8　Explain how to play using the instructions below.

9　Now the students are ready to play the game. While they are playing, go round to each group and check they are playing correctly.

HOW TO PLAY THE GAME

1　Each player takes four complaint cards and two advice cards.

2　Player A puts down a card showing the first half of a complaint.

3　Player B must complete the complaint correctly using one of his/her cards.

4　Player C puts down a card showing a piece of advice for the complaint. If it is correct, he/she keeps the three cards and puts down the first half of a new complaint.

5　If a player cannot put down a correct card, he/she picks one up from the appropriate pile on the table and the next player puts down a card.

6　When all the cards are finished, the player with the most cards is the winner.

TEAM A

Q: The Pacific Ocean is bigger than the continent of Asia. **True** or **false**?

A: **True.** The Pacific is three times bigger than Asia.

Q: A Jumbo jet flies higher than Concorde. **True** or **false**?

A: **False.** A Jumbo jet flies up to 12 km high and Concorde flies up to 18 km high.

Q: Which mountain is higher: Mount Kilimanjaro in Africa or Mont Blanc in France?

A: **Mount Kilimanjaro** is 5895 m high, Mont Blanc is 4810 m high.

Q: Which is the largest desert in the world: is it the Sahara of North Africa, the desert of Patagonia in South America or the Gobi desert of Central Asia?

A: **The Sahara** covers 8 400 000 sq km, the desert of Patagonia covers 670 000 sq km and the Gobi desert, 1 040 000 sq km.

Q: There are more sheep in Australia than people. **True** or **false**?

A: **True.**

Q: Which mountain range is older: the Urals in Russia or the Highlands of Scotland?

A: **The Highlands** are 400 million years old, the Urals are 250 million years old.

Q: The most expensive land in the world is in the centre of Hong Kong. **True** or **false**?

A: **True.** It costs $180 000 per sq metre to rent.

Q: The shortest scheduled flight in the world lasts nine and a half minutes. **True** or **false**?

A: **False.** The shortest scheduled flight (in Scotland) lasts two minutes.

Q: Death Valley in North America is the driest place in the world. **True** or **false**?

A: **False.** Death Valley is the driest place in North America, but the Atacama in northern Chile is the driest place on Earth.

Q: The tallest iceberg above water was as tall as the Eiffel Tower, Paris. **True** or **false**?

A: **False.** It was half as tall as the Eiffel Tower.

Q: The largest active volcano on earth is in Hawaii. **True** or **false**?

A: **True.** Mauna Loa, in Hawaii, is 4168 m high.

Q: The oldest country in the world is Egypt. **True** or **false**?

A: **False.** Iran has been an independent country since the 6th century BC.

Q: The highest capital city in the world is La Paz in Bolivia. **True** or **false**?

A: **True.** It is 3625 m high in the Andes.

Q: The largest wheatfield in the world is as big as 2000 football pitches. **True** or **false**?

A: **False.** The largest wheatfield is in Canada and is as big as 20 000 football pitches.

Q: Greenland is the largest island in the world. **True** or **false**?

A: **True.** It is nearly 10 times larger than Britain.

Q: The tallest tree on earth is taller than the Statue of Liberty in New York. **True** or **false**?

A: **True.** The tallest tree, the giant redwood, is 112 m high and the Statue of Liberty is 93 m high.

Q: Which city has the longest underground: New York, Tokyo or London?

A: **London** has 400 km of underground.

Q: Where is the largest hotel in the world: is it in New York, Moscow or Sydney?

A: **It's in Moscow.** The Hotel Rossiya has 3200 rooms.

Q: Toe nails grow faster than finger nails. **True** or **false**?

A: **False.** Finger nails grow faster than toe nails.

Q: The wettest place in the world is Liverpool, England. **True** or **false**?

A: **False.** Mount Wai-'ale-'ale in Hawaii is the wettest place – it rains 335 days a year.

World quiz **Worksheets 29a and 29b**

NOTE: Use Worksheets 29a and 29b for this activity.

ACTIVITY
Groupwork: speaking

AIM
To play a game of noughts and crosses by choosing the correct answers to questions about world facts.

GRAMMAR AND FUNCTIONS
Comparative and superlative forms of short adjectives

VOCABULARY
World facts

PREPARATION
Make one copy of Worksheets 29a and 29b for each group of four to six students in the class.

TIME
30 minutes

PROCEDURE
1 Draw a noughts and crosses grid on the board and ask a student to come to the board to play a game with you.

2 When one of you has got a line of noughts or crosses, explain to the students that they are going to play the same game, but that they can only put a nought or cross on the grid if they answer a question correctly.

3 Ask the students to work in groups of four or six and to divide their groups into two teams, Team A and Team B.

4 Give one copy of Team A questions to each Team A and a copy of Team B questions to each Team B.

5 Each group draws a noughts and crosses grid on a piece of paper and then decides which team is going to be noughts and which is going to be crosses.

6 A member of Team A reads out a question from their question sheet to Team B. If Team B give the correct answer, they choose a square on the grid and put a nought or a cross in it. It is now Team B's turn to read out a question from their question sheet for Team A to answer.

7 Continue like this, with teams taking it in turns to ask and answer questions, until one team gets a line of noughts or crosses. They score one point for getting a line.

8 Play the game again until all the questions have been answered. The team with the highest score is the winner.

TEAM B

Q: Concorde flies faster than the speed of light. **True** or **false**?

A: **False.** Concorde flies faster than the speed of sound.

Q: Which is harder: quartz or diamond?

A: **Diamond** is the hardest mineral on Earth.

Q: Which is the longest mountain range: the Himalayas of Asia or the Andes of South America?

A: **The Andes** are 7243 km long, the Himalayas are 3860 km long.

Q: Which waterfall is higher: the Angel Falls in Venezuela or the Tugela Falls in South Africa?

A: **The Angel Falls** are 979 m high. The Tugela Falls are 948 m high.

Q: The worst place for earthquakes is Japan. **True** or **false**?

A: **False.** China has the worst record for earthquake deaths. In 1976, an earthquake killed 750 000 people.

Q: The smallest country in the world is Monaco. **True** or **false**?

A: **False.** The smallest country is the Vatican City.

Q: Which city has the longest full name: Beijing, Cardiff or Bangkok?

A: **Bangkok.** Its full name has 167 letters.

Q: The widest road in the world is in Brazil. **True** or **false**?

A: **True.** It is the Monumental Axis in Brasilia and it is 250 m wide.

Q: Where is the largest art gallery in the world: is it in Italy, Spain or Russia?

A: **Russia** (the Winter Palace in St Petersburg).

Q: Where is the smallest professional theatre in the world: is it in Lisbon, Hamburg or Reykjavik?

A: **Hamburg.** The Piccolo holds only 30 people.

Q: There are more cattle in New Zealand than people. **True** or **false**?

A: **True.**

Q: There are more cats in the USA than sheep in Australia. **True** or **false**?

A: **False**, but there are more cats in the USA than people in Australia.

Q: Penguins can swim faster than humans. **True** or **false**?

A: **True.** They can swim four times faster than humans.

Q: Sunflowers can grow as tall as giraffes. **True** or **false**?

A: **True.**

Q: The tallest statue in the world is the Statue of Liberty in New York. **True** or **false**?

A: **False.** The tallest statue is the Buddha in Tokyo, Japan, and it is 120 m high. The Statue of Liberty is 93 m high.

Q: The largest animal is the African elephant. **True** or **false**?

A: **False.** The largest animal is the blue whale.

Q: The biggest bird is the ostrich. **True** or **false**?

A: **True.**

Q: The largest lived-in palace in the world is Buckingham Palace in London. **True** or **false**?

A: **False.** The palace of the Sultan of Brunei has 1788 rooms and 257 toilets.

Q: Bombay in India is wetter than Rome in Italy. **True** or **false**?

A: **True.** In an average year, more rain falls in Bombay than in Rome.

Q: The longest alphabet in the world has 74 letters. **True** or **false**?

A: **True.** It is used in Cambodia.

Who lives in the most beautiful place?

FIND OUT

Who plays the most dangerous sport?

FIND OUT

Who has the most interesting ambition?

FIND OUT

Who had the busiest weekend?

FIND OUT

Who had the healthiest breakfast this morning?

FIND OUT

Who has the smallest pet?

FIND OUT

Who has the best singing voice?

FIND OUT

Who has the most tiring lifestyle?

FIND OUT

Who has the oldest grandparent?

FIND OUT

Who has the youngest brother or sister?

FIND OUT

Who has the most expensive hobby?

FIND OUT

Who has the longest journey to work/school?

FIND OUT

Find the person with the most... Worksheet 30

ACTIVITY
Whole class: speaking

AIM
To find out information about members of the class by asking and answering questions.

GRAMMAR AND FUNCTIONS
Comparative and superlative forms of short and longer adjectives

VOCABULARY
Adjectives to describe people, everyday activities and leisure activities

PREPARATION
Make one copy of the worksheet for each group of up to 12 students. Cut the cards out as indicated.

TIME
15 to 20 minutes

PROCEDURE

1 If there are more than 12 students in the class, divide them into groups. Give one card to each student in the class.

2 Tell the students that they are responsible for finding the answer to the question on their own card by speaking to everybody in the class or group. Make sure each student knows how to ask their question correctly and give them some time to think about the questions they need to ask. For example:

On the card: *Who lives in the most beautiful place? Find out.*

Questions: *Where do you live? What's it like?*

3 Now ask the students to go round the class or group asking and answering questions. Tell them that they can make notes on the back of their card if necessary.

4 When they have finished, they should sit down with two or three students from the same group, discuss the information they have gathered and come to a group decision about the answers to the questions on their cards. At this stage, encourage them to use the language of comparison. For example:

Student A: *I think basketball is more dangerous than swimming.*

Student B: *Well, I can't swim, so I think swimming is more dangerous than basketball!*

5 When they have finished, they should tell the rest of the class the answers to the questions on their cards.

FOLLOW-UP
Ask the students to stay in their groups and to write the information they have gathered on a poster to be displayed in the classroom. For example:

In our group ...
> *Hélène lives in the most beautiful place. She lives in Paris.*
> *Stefano plays the most dangerous sport. He plays rugby.*
> *Miki has the most interesting ambition. She wants to be the first woman on the moon.*

26-30 | *Think of a word*

WORD ....

Something bigger _____

Something smaller _____

A verb that goes with it _____

A word that comes earlier in the dictionary _____

A longer word beginning with the same letter _____

A shorter word beginning with the same letter _____

An adjective to describe it _____

The opposite of that adjective _____

Another word the adjectives go with _____

✂ ....

WORD ....

Something bigger _____

Something smaller _____

A verb that goes with it _____

A word that comes earlier in the dictionary _____

A longer word beginning with the same letter _____

A shorter word beginning with the same letter _____

An adjective to describe it _____

The opposite of that adjective _____

Another word the adjectives go with _____

PHOTOCOPIABLE

Think of a word Worksheet Progress check 26-30

ACTIVITY
Groupwork: writing, speaking

AIM
To play a game by finding words in given categories.

GRAMMAR AND FUNCTIONS
Comparative forms

VOCABULARY
General

PREPARATION
Make one copy of the worksheet for each group of three to five students in the class.

TIME
30 minutes

PROCEDURE

1   Write any noun on the board.
    For example:
    elephant

    Now ask the students to suggest the following:
        something bigger: for example, *a jumbo jet*
        something smaller: for example, *a mouse*
        a verb that goes with it: for example, *ride*
        a word that comes earlier in the dictionary: for
            example, *donkey*
        a longer word beginning with the same letter: for
            example, *examination*
        a shorter word beginning with the same letter: for
            example, *egg*
        an adjective to describe it: for example, *big*
        the opposite of that adjective: *small*
        another word the adjectives go with: for example,
            house

2   Now ask the students to work in groups of three to five
    and tell them that they are going to do the same thing in
    their groups.

3   Give each group a copy of the worksheet.

4   Tell them that you are going to write a word on the board
    and that they have to write words on one of the charts on
    their worksheet in the spaces provided, according to the
    instructions. Tell them that they must do it as quickly as
    possible and that you will stop the activity as soon as one
    of the groups has found a word for each category.

5   Write a word on the board. The following are some
    examples of words you can use:
        apple   lorry   house   teacher   plane   train
        horse   banana   football   sandwich
        newspaper   cigarette   desk   bath   umbrella
        grape   ice cream   window   door   boot
        guitar   television   bicycle   chair   sweater
        mountain   piano   wallet   postcard
        hamburger   stamp   suitcase

6   As soon as one group finishes, stop the activity.

7   Check the answers. Each group gets one point for a word
    which is correct and different from the other groups'
    words for that category.

8   The group with the highest score is the winner.

9   Play as many rounds of the game as you like, using a
    different word each time and providing more copies of the
    chart if necessary.

OPTION
To make the activity easier, allow the students to use a
dictionary.

Guess the place **Worksheet** 31

ACTIVITY
Whole class: writing, speaking

AIM
To write down what you can and can't do in places and to guess what the places are by reading the rules.

GRAMMAR AND FUNCTIONS
Must, mustn't

VOCABULARY
General

PREPARATION
Make one copy of the worksheet for each group of up to ten students. Cut the cards out as indicated.

TIME
20 minutes

PROCEDURE

1 Think of a place where customs and rules must be followed and write some example sentences on the board without mentioning the place you have in mind.
For example:

> *You mustn't ride a bicycle.*
> *You mustn't stop.*
> *You mustn't fall asleep.*
> *You mustn't drive faster than the limit.*
> *In some countries you must pay.*

Ask the students to guess what the place is. (A motorway.)

2 Tell them that they are going to write similar sentences about other places.

3 If there are more than ten students in the class, divide them into groups. Give one card to each student in the class. Tell the students not to show their own picture to the other students in their group.

4 Ask the students to write sentences about the place on their own card on the back of the card. The sentences should begin *You must* or *You mustn't*. While they are doing this, be on hand to answer questions and offer help.

5 When they have done this, ask them to go round the class or group, working with as many different partners as possible. They should take it in turns to read out their sentences to one another, making sure that their picture is hidden, and to guess their partner's place. When they have guessed correctly, they should change partner.

6 The students continue until they have worked with as many different partners as possible.

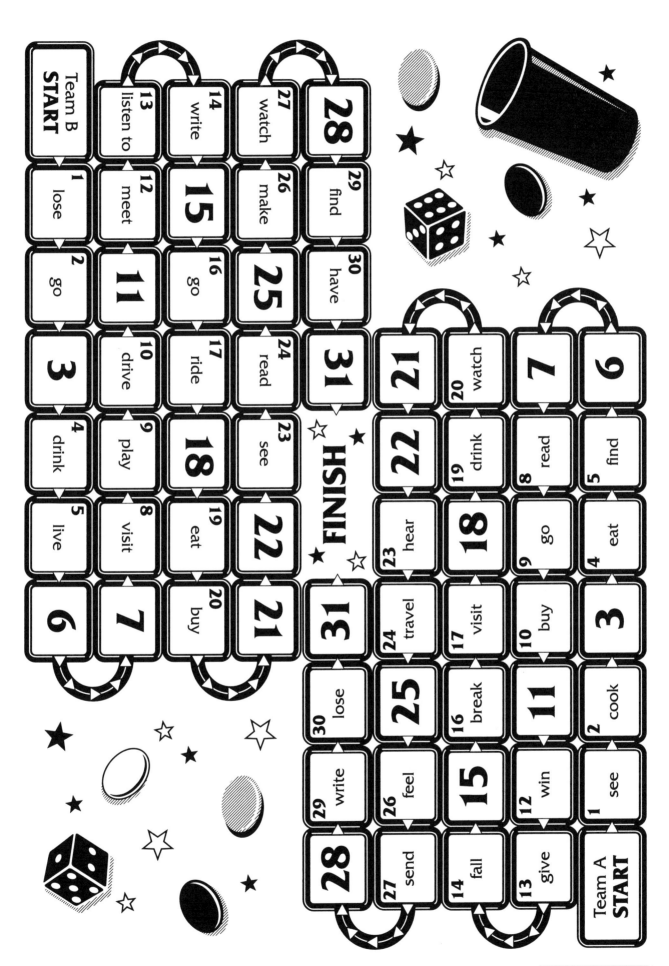

Have you ever...? Worksheet 32

ACTIVITY
Groupwork: writing, speaking

AIM
To play a game by asking and answering questions about experiences.

GRAMMAR AND FUNCTIONS
Present perfect to talk about experiences
Past simple to talk about a definite time in the past

VOCABULARY
Past participles of regular and irregular verbs

PREPARATION
Make one copy of the game board for every six students in the class. Provide dice and counters for each group.

TIME
1 hour

PROCEDURE
1 Ask the students to work in groups of six and to divide their groups into two teams, Team A and Team B.

2 Tell them that they are going to play a game but that before they do, you are going to give each team a list of verbs and they are going to prepare some questions using these verbs.

3 Write an example question on the board, using *Have you ever*.
For example:
   lose: *Have you ever lost your keys?*

4 Ask students the example question and if a student answers *Yes, I have*, ask for additional information.

For example:
   When did you lose them?
   Were they car keys or house keys?
   Did you find them again?

5 Repeat procedure points 3 and 4 using one of Team B's verbs.

6 Give the following list of verbs to each Team A:
   lose   go   drink   live   visit   play   drive
   meet   listen to   write   go   ride   eat   buy
   see   read   make   watch   find   have

   Give the following list of verbs to each Team B:
   see   cook   eat   find   read   go   buy
   win   give   fall   break   visit   drink   watch
   hear   travel   feel   send   write   lose

7 Now tell the students that they are going to write a question beginning *Have you ever* and an additional question in the simple past for each of the verbs on their list. Tell them to choose one member of the team to write down the questions.

   Alternatively, if you wanted to speed up this part of the activity, the three students in each team could divide the verbs out between them and write the sentences individually.

   While the students are doing this, be on hand to answer questions and offer help.

8 When they have done that, give one copy of the worksheet to each group of students and explain how to play the game using the instructions below.

9 The students are now ready to play the game. While they are playing, go round to each group and check they are playing correctly.

HOW TO PLAY THE GAME

1 Put the game board in the middle of the table.

2 Each team places their counter on the squares marked START.

3 Player 1 from Team A throws the dice and moves the counter along the board according to the number on the dice.

4 If the counter lands on a square with a number only, Player 1 from Team B throws the dice.

5 If Team A's counter lands on a square with a verb, Player 1 from Team B reads out the question they have prepared using that verb. Player 1 from Team A must answer *Yes, I have*, whether this is true or false. Player 1 from Team B then asks the question requiring further information. Player

1 from Team A gives a true answer to the question if he/she has had the experience or invents an answer if he/she has not had the experience. Team B then guess whether the answer is true or false.

6 If they guess correctly, it is Team B's turn to throw the dice and move their counter along the board.

7 If they do not guess correctly, Team A can throw the dice and move their counter again. Players must promise to be honest and not cheat!

8 The game continues with players from each team taking it in turns to ask and answer questions until the first team reaches the square marked FINISH. This team is the winner.

fold ✂ fold

✂

worried

tell / the police?

lose / my wallet

ill

call / the doctor?

hurt / my back

unhappy

make / an appointment to see the dentist?

break / a tooth

happy

spend / it?

win / £100 on the lottery

worried

buy / a present?

remember / my mother's birthday

tired

have / breakfast?

get / up

happy

ask / him/her out?

fall / in love

worried

report / it?

see / an accident

happy

wear / it?

buy / a new coat

happy

buy / a new one?

sell / my car

I've just... Worksheet 33

ACTIVITY
Whole class: speaking
Mill drill (For detailed instructions and advice on using mill drills, see the notes for teachers at the beginning of the Resource Pack.)

AIM
To speak to as many partners as possible, using pictures as prompts to talk about something which has just happened.

GRAMMAR AND FUNCTIONS
Present perfect to talk about recent events: *just* and *yet*

VOCABULARY
General

PREPARATION
Make one copy of the worksheet for each group of up to ten students and cut the cards out, being careful to cut and fold as indicated. You will need to keep one card for yourself to demonstrate the activity.

TIME
15 minutes

PROCEDURE

1 If there are more than ten students in the class, divide them into groups. Give one folded card to each student in the class. Keep one for yourself.

2 Tell the students that they are going to talk about things that have just happened, using their cards as prompts. Write an example dialogue on the board, indicating the language the students should use.
For example:
    Student A: *You look worried. What's happened?*
    Student B: *I've just lost my wallet.*
    Student A: *Have you told the police yet?*
    Student B: *Not yet, but I'm going to.*

3 Demonstrate the activity with individual students, using the card you kept for yourself. Tell the students to hold their cards so that the picture showing the action which has just happened is facing them and the picture of the face is facing their partner. Their partner begins *You look...*. Ask several pairs of students to demonstrate the activity to the whole class, using their pictures as prompts.

4 Now ask the students to go round the class or group and ask and answer questions with as many different partners as possible, using their picture cards as prompts. In this part of the activity, the students ask different questions each time they change partner, but give the same answer.

5 When the students have finished, ask them to exchange cards and to go round the class or group again, this time holding their cards the other way round so that the picture showing the action which has just happened is facing their partner and the face is facing them. The students take it in turns to ask and answer questions using their picture cards as prompts. In this part of the activity, the students ask the same question several times, but give a different answer each time they change partner.

6 The students continue asking and answering in this way until they have spoken to as many different partners as possible.

What do
people do to
relax?

Find out.

What do
people do to
keep fit?

Find out.

What do
people do to
get rid of a
headache?

Find out.

What do
people do to
improve their
English?

Find out.

Where do
people go to
have a good
night out?

Find out.

Where do
people go to
eat a delicious
meal?

Find out.

Where do
people go to
buy clothes?

Find out.

What do
people do to
help the
environment?

Find out.

What do
people do to
celebrate
birthdays?

Find out.

What do
people do to
remember
things?

Find out.

Purposeful activities Worksheet 34

ACTIVITY
Whole class: speaking

AIM
To find out information about people by asking and answering questions.

GRAMMAR AND FUNCTIONS
Infinitive of purpose

VOCABULARY
Routine activities

PREPARATION
Make one copy of the worksheet for each group of up to ten students. Cut the cards out as indicated.

TIME
15 to 20 minutes

PROCEDURE
1 If there are more than ten students in the class, divide them into groups. Give one card to each student in the class.

2 Tell the students that they are responsible for finding the answer to the question on their own card by speaking to everybody in their group. Make sure the students know how to formulate the question correctly.
For example:
Student A: *What do you do to relax?*
Student B: *I listen to classical music.*
What do you do to keep fit?
Student A: *I walk to work every day.*

3 Now ask the students to go round the class or group asking and answering questions. Tell them that they may need to make notes on a separate piece of paper.

4 When they have spoken to everybody in the class or group, they should take it in turns to report back to the class or group on the information they have found out.

FOLLOW-UP
Ask the students to work with one or two other students in their group and to write the information they have gathered on a poster to be displayed in the classroom.
For example:
Several people in the class watch television to relax.
Pobchai paints, Marie-Louise listens to classical music and Yuko does yoga.
Salmina, Miki and Carlos go to the gym to keep fit.
Bruno and Ahmed play football, and Elif walks to work every day.

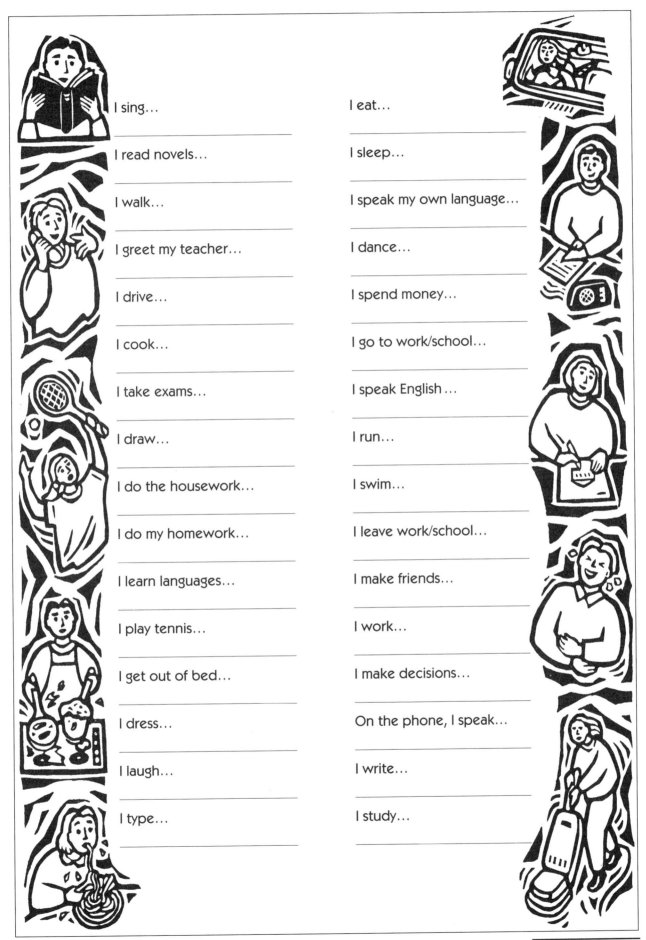

I sing…

I read novels…

I walk…

I greet my teacher…

I drive…

I cook…

I take exams…

I draw…

I do the housework…

I do my homework…

I learn languages…

I play tennis…

I get out of bed…

I dress…

I laugh…

I type…

I eat…

I sleep…

I speak my own language…

I dance…

I spend money…

I go to work/school…

I speak English…

I run…

I swim…

I leave work/school…

I make friends…

I work…

I make decisions…

On the phone, I speak…

I write…

I study…

I do it my way Worksheet **35**

ACTIVITY
Pairwork: writing, speaking

AIM
To talk about the way people do everyday activities and to guess what the activities are.

GRAMMAR AND FUNCTIONS
Adverbs

VOCABULARY
Adverbs
Everyday activities

PREPARATION
Make one copy of the worksheet for each student in the class.

TIME
20 minutes

PROCEDURE

1 Give one copy of the worksheet to each student in the class.

2 Ask them to choose ten incomplete sentences from their worksheet and to complete them in any way true for themselves by adding an appropriate adverb.
For example:
I sing badly.
I read novels slowly.
I eat very quickly.

They must use a different adverb for each activity. Brainstorm adverbs before the students start the activity if necessary. They should not let the other students see what they are writing.

3 When they have finished, tell the students that you are going to tell them how *you* do something and they must guess which of the activities on their worksheet you are referring to.
For example:
It's something I do well. (speak English)
It's something I do loudly. (laugh)

4 Now ask the students to work in pairs and tell them that they are going to take it in turns to tell their partner how they do an activity and to guess what their partner's activities are. They should read them out in the same way as in the example above.

5 Students can have five tries at guessing each activity. They can score 5 points for guessing the first time, 4 points for guessing the second time, 3 points for the third time, etc. If a student hasn't guessed after five tries, their partner scores 5 points.

6 The student with the highest score is the winner.

A **CLUES ACROSS**

Example

3 You go there to have a drink.

5 _____

7 _____

9 _____

10 _____

12 _____

13 _____

14 _____

16 _____

19 _____

20 _____

21 _____

B **CLUES DOWN**

Example

1 You drive over it to cross a river.

2 _____

4 _____

5 _____

6 _____

8 _____

10 _____

11 _____

14 _____

15 _____

17 _____

18 _____

PHOTOCOPIABLE

Crossword **Worksheet Progress check** 31-35

ACTIVITY
Pairwork: speaking, writing

AIM
To write clues for a crossword and to complete it.

GRAMMAR AND FUNCTIONS
Infinitive of purpose

VOCABULARY
Everyday objects
Places

PREPARATION
Make one copy of the worksheet for each pair of students in the class and cut it out as indicated.

TIME
40 minutes

PROCEDURE
1 Tell the students that you are going to give them a definition of a word, and that they have to guess what the word is. Write 'You go there to have a drink' on the board. Elicit the answer: 'pub'. Now write 'You drive over it to cross a river.' Elicit the answer: 'bridge'. Tell the students that they are going to write similar definitions of words as clues for a crossword.

2 Divide the class into Group A and Group B.

3 Explain that you are going to give both groups the same crossword but that Group A will have the across words already written in and Group B will have the down words already written in. Their task is to write clues for the words written on their crosswords.

4 Give a copy of crossword A to each student in Group A and a copy of crossword B to each student in Group B.

5 Ask the students to work with two or three other students from the same group. They should invent and write down clues for the words on their crossword in the spaces provided. Encourage them to use the target language. All the students should write the clues down on their own worksheet.

6 When they have finished writing their clues, the students should work with a partner from the other group (ie a student from Group A should work with a student from Group B). They must not show their crossword to their partner.

7 Ask the students to sit facing one another and take it in turns to ask their partner for clues to the missing words on their own crossword. They should read out the clues they have written for their partner to guess the words, and write in the missing words on their crosswords from the clues their partner gives them.

ANSWER

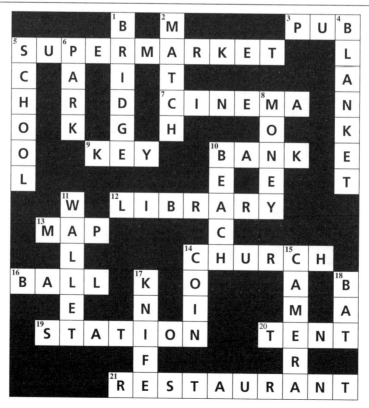

DESK	DEPARTURE	LOUNGE	ARRIVAL
HALL	BOARDING	PASS	PASSPORT
CONTROL	BAGGAGE	RECLAIM	TOURIST
CLASS	CHEAP DAY	RETURN	WAITING
ROOM	TICKET	OFFICE	CREDIT
CARD	TAXI	RANK	CAR
HIRE	SMOKING	AREA	INFORMATION

PHOTOCOPIABLE

Travel dominoes Worksheet 36

ACTIVITY
Groupwork: speaking

AIM
To play a game of dominoes by matching words that go together.

GRAMMAR AND FUNCTIONS
Collocation

VOCABULARY
Words associated with rail and air travel

PREPARATION
Make one copy of the worksheet for each group of three students in the class and cut out all the cards as indicated.

TIME
15 minutes

PROCEDURE

1 Explain to the students that they are going to play a game of dominoes by matching words that go together, for example *departure lounge*, *arrival hall* etc, and that the object of the game is to get rid of all their dominoes.

2 Ask the students to work in groups of three and give each group of students a set of dominoes. Ask them to deal out three dominoes each and to leave the rest in a pile, face down.

3 Before they start, explain how to play using the instructions below.

4 The students are ready to play the game. While they are playing, go round to each group and check they are playing correctly.

5 When they have finished a game, they can shuffle and play another round.

HOW TO PLAY THE GAME

1 Player A puts down any one of their dominoes face up.

2 The player on their left must then put down one of their dominoes, making sure that one of the words on their domino matches one of the words on either side of Player A's domino.
For example:
Domino A: DESK / DEPARTURE
Domino B: either INFORMATION or LOUNGE

3 If a player cannot put down one of their dominoes, they take a domino from the top of the pile and put it down if they can.

4 The winner is the first player to get rid of all of their dominoes.

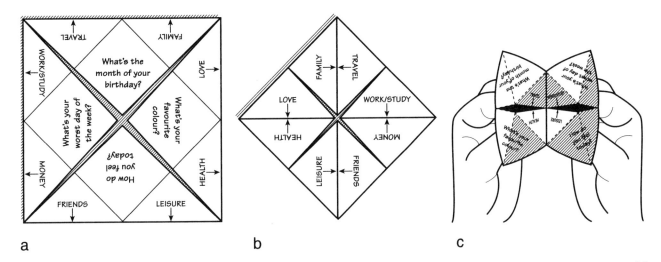

a   b   c

What's the month of your birthday?

TRAVEL

WORK/STUDY

What's your worst day of the week?

FAMILY

MONEY

LOVE

FRIENDS

What's your favourite colour?

HEALTH

LEISURE

How do you feel today?

PHOTOCOPIABLE

Predictogram Worksheet 37

ACTIVITY
Whole class: writing, speaking

AIM
To play a game by writing and reading out predictions.

GRAMMAR AND FUNCTIONS
Future simple for predictions
Instructions

VOCABULARY
General

PREPARATION
Make one copy of the worksheet for each student in the class. You will need to provide scissors for this activity.

TIME
30 minutes

PROCEDURE
1 Write the following headings on the board:
health, love, family, travel, work/study, money, friends, leisure

2 Ask the students to make predictions for you under these headings.
For example:

    health: *You will have a headache this afternoon.*
    love: *You will meet someone special on holiday.*
    family: *You will receive a letter from a member of your family at the weekend.*

3 Now tell the students that they are going to make a 'predictogram' and use it to make similar predictions for one another.

4 Give one copy of the worksheet to each student in the class. Tell them to write one prediction in the space provided under each heading on their worksheet. They do not have to have a reader in mind at this stage. While they are doing this, be on hand to answer questions and offer help. Encourage the students to use the target language.

5 When they have done that, tell the students that they are going to prepare their predictogram. Read out the instructions below.

NOTE: It is a good idea for you to try this out yourself before doing it with the class and then demonstrate as you read out the instructions.

HOW TO PREPARE THE PREDICTOGRAM

1 Cut out the square as indicated on the worksheet.

2 Fold the square in half diagonally along one of the dotted lines in the centre of the square.

3 Open the square out again and fold it in half diagonally along the other dotted line in the centre.

4 Open the square out and turn it over so that the writing is face down.

5 Fold each corner of the square to the middle of the square. The category headings are now face up. (fig. a)

6 Turn the square over so that the predictions are face up and the category headings are face down.

7 Fold the new corners into the middle of the square. Now the category headings are face up and the four questions are face down. (fig. b)

8 Fold the square in half and open it again.

9 Fold it in half the other way and open it again.

10 Now put the forefinger and thumb of each hand under the flaps with the questions on and push up so that the questions are face up. (fig. c)

11 Finally, explain how to play the game, using the instructions below.

12 The students are now ready to play the game. While they are playing, go round to each group and check they are playing correctly.

HOW TO PLAY THE GAME

1 Ask a partner to choose one of the questions and answer it.
For example:
    What's your favourite colour?

If the answer is, for example, green, spell out the word, opening and closing the predictogram alternate ways for each letter: G-R-E-E-N.

2 Now ask your partner to choose one of the four categories showing inside the predictogram.

3 When they have chosen a category, open the predictogram out and read out the corresponding prediction.

4 Repeat the activity with different partners.

Paper was invented	in China nearly 2000 years ago.
The first guitar was made	by a Spanish instrument maker.
Pasta and ice cream were first made	in China.
Van Gogh's painting, 'Sunflowers', was bought	by a Japanese company.
More wine is produced in Italy than	in France.
The first underground railway was opened	in London in 1863.
The first nuclear power station was opened	in Russia in 1954.
The first pair of jeans was made	by a German tailor called Levi Strauss.
The Volkswagen 'Beetle' was designed	by Ferdinand Porsche.
869 languages are spoken	in Papua New Guinea.
The ballpoint pen was invented	by a Hungarian called Biro.
Mirrors were invented	by the Egyptians.
The rubber tyre was invented	by John Dunlop in 1888.
Toothpaste was invented	by the Romans in 960.
The first tape cassettes were designed	by a Dutch company.
The raincoat was invented	by a Scotsman called Charles Macintosh.
The first modern Olympic Games were played	in 1896.
The first World Cup was held	in 1930.
Each year 3000 million flowers are grown	in Holland.
The first motorcycle was built	by a French company in 1869.

PHOTOCOPIABLE

Did you know...? Worksheet **38**

ACTIVITY
Groupwork: speaking, reading

AIM
To match two parts of a sentence.

GRAMMAR AND FUNCTIONS
Present and past passive

VOCABULARY
Inventions and other world facts

PREPARATION
Make one copy of the worksheet for each group of three or four students in the class and cut it up into cards as indicated. Make one copy of the worksheet for each group of three or four students and leave it intact.

TIME
20 to 30 minutes

PROCEDURE

1   Write on the board 'Paper was invented ...' and ask the students if they can complete the sentence with information about *where* or *when* it was invented. When they have guessed the answer, tell them that they can confirm whether they were right or wrong by doing the activity.

2   Explain that you are going to give them 20 sentences, but that each sentence is in two parts. Their task is to find 20 facts by finding the two parts of each sentence which go together correctly.

3   Ask the students to work in groups of three or four and give one set of cards to each group.

4   Tell the students to shuffle their cards and then spread them out, face up, on the table.

5   Tell them that they have got five minutes to find 20 facts.

6   When they have done that, give one intact copy of the worksheet to each group of students so that they can check their answers.

7   Now tell the students to pick the cards up in two piles, one with the first halves of the sentences written on them and the other with the place, date or person's name written on them. They should shuffle each pile of cards and then spread them out separately, face down on the table.

8   Now ask the students to take it in turns to turn over one card from each pile. If the two cards go together to make a correct fact, the student reads it out aloud, keeps the two cards and plays again. If they do not go together, the student reads it out aloud, but turns it into a negative statement.
For example:
   Paper wasn't invented by a Spanish instrument maker.

They then turn the two cards back over and another student in the group repeats the procedure.

9   The students continue in this way until all the cards have been used up. The student with the most cards at the end of the activity is the winner.

IDEAL PARTNER　　　　✔ = YES　　　　✗ = NO

Is it important for your partner to be

– good-looking?

– kind?

– the same religion as you?

– intelligent?

– a good cook?

– funny?

HOPES AND DREAMS　　　　✔ = YES　　　　✗ = NO

Do you want to

– be a millionnaire?

– get married and have children?

– travel and meet people?

– be famous?

– play a sport for your country?

– run your own business?

SPARE TIME　　　　✔ = YES　　　　✗ = NO

In the last month, have you

– watched television or a video?

– been shopping for food?

– read a book?

– done some gardening?

– been to a restaurant?

– played a sport?

CULTURE　　　　✔ = YES　　　　✗ = NO

In the last month, have you been to

– a library?

– the cinema?

– a museum?

– the theatre?

– a football match?

– a concert?

PHOTOCOPIABLE

Class survey Worksheets **39a** and **39b**

NOTE: Use Worksheets 39a and 39b for this activity.

ACTIVITY
Pairwork and groupwork: speaking, writing

AIM
To do a class survey by asking and answering questions and to report the results of the survey.

GRAMMAR AND FUNCTIONS
Reported speech: statements
... *said that* + clause

VOCABULARY
General

PREPARATION
Make one copy of Worksheets 39a and 39b for every 16 students in the class and cut the cards out as indicated.

TIME
30 to 40 minutes

PROCEDURE

1   Explain to the students that they are going to do a class survey and explain what a survey is, if necessary.

2   If there are more than 16 students in the class, divide them into groups. Ask the students to work with a partner from the same group and give one card to each pair of students.

3   Explain that each pair of students is responsible for asking everybody in the class or group all the questions on their card. They should put a tick each time somebody answers *yes* and a cross each time somebody answers *no* to one of the questions.

4   Now ask the students to go round the class or group in pairs asking and answering questions and putting ticks or crosses on their card.

5   When they have spoken to everybody in the class or group, ask them to write the information they have gathered on a poster under the following headings:
    Nobody said that ...
    A few people said that ...
    A lot of people said that ...
    Everybody said that ...

    For example:
SURVEY RESULTS: HOPES AND DREAMS

Nobody said that ...	A few people said that ...
... they wanted to play a sport for their own country.	... they wanted to be famous. ... they wanted to run their own business.
A lot of people said that ...	Everybody said that ...
... they wanted to get married and have children. ... they wanted to travel and meet people.	... they wanted to be a millionnaire.

6   Encourage the students to use the target language and be on hand to answer questions and offer help at this stage.

7   Ask the pairs of students to take it in turns to read out their survey results to the rest of the group or class.

FOOD AND DRINK   ✔ = YES   ✗ = NO

Do you

– drink more than three glasses of water a day?

– eat a big breakfast?

– eat meat every day?

– eat some fruit every day?

– drink more than three cups of coffee or tea a day?

– often go to a restaurant?

WORRIES   ✔ = YES   ✗ = NO

Are you worried about

– your health?

– money?

– world war?

– growing old?

– your job/studies?

– the environment?

NEXT WEEKEND   ✔ = YES   ✗ = NO

Are you going to

– get up late?

– go dancing?

– go shopping?

– study?

– travel to a different town?

– visit family or friends?

LAST WEEKEND   ✔ = YES   ✗ = NO

Did you

– have a busy weekend?

– go away?

– write any letters?

– go to a disco?

– go to the cinema?

– play any sport?

PHOTOCOPIABLE

TELL YOUR
GROUP...

START

FINISH

Board game spaces (clockwise from start):

- what you're going to eat tonight
- what you usually have for breakfast
- about a good film you've seen
- three things you did before you left your house this morning
- about a book you're reading at the moment
- about what you bought last week
- what you're going to wear tomorrow
- about your mother's typical day
- what fruit you ate yesterday
- about a good friend of yours
- about your typical Sunday
- about the watch you're wearing
- where you think you'll be in five years' time
- what you're going to do next weekend
- three sports you've never tried
- where you usually go for a night out
- what you think you'll look like in ten years' time
- about the best holiday you've had
- five countries you haven't visited yet but would like to
- something you're going to learn in the future
- about the last time you ate ice cream
- about the best restaurant you've been to
- what a member of your family is doing at the moment
- the first thing you're going to do when you get home
- about your last birthday
- what you're going to do after this lesson

Tell your group... Worksheet **40**

ACTIVITY
Groupwork: speaking

AIM
To play a board game by talking about given topics.

GRAMMAR AND FUNCTIONS
Tense review

VOCABULARY
General

PREPARATION
Make one copy of the worksheet (game board) for every three to five students in the class. Provide dice and counters for each group.

TIME
30 minutes

PROCEDURE
1 Ask the students to work in groups of three to five.

2 Give one game board, some counters and dice to each group.

3 Before the students start playing the game, explain how to play using the instructions below.

4 It is important to remind the students to be careful to use the appropriate tense when they are talking about a topic. In particular, remind them that if the topic on the game board is written in the present perfect, they will need to use the simple past when they refer to a specific time in the past. For example, if the topic is 'The best holiday you've had', they will need to use the simple past to talk about it: *I went to..., I saw ...*, etc.

5 The students are ready to play the game. While they are playing, go round to each group and check that they are using the tenses correctly.

HOW TO PLAY THE GAME

1 Put the game board in the middle of the table.

2 All the players put their counters on the square marked START and throw the dice. The first player to throw a six starts the game.

3 Player A throws the dice and moves their counter along the board according to the number on the dice.

4 Player A then reads the topic on the square the counter has landed on and talks about it.

5 If a player has nothing to say on the topic they have landed on, they are allowed to pass and miss a turn, but they can only do this once in the game.

6 The game continues until the first player reaches the square marked FINISH.

36-40 | *Find the mistake*

STUDENT A

1 They've got one daughter and she's doctor.

2 English is speaking by 350 million people in the world.

3 I go to work by bus and it only takes five minutes because I live very near the office.

4 I like play football but I've broken my leg so I can't do any sport at the moment.

5 I can't answer the telephone because I'm washing my hair.

6 'Let's have fish and chips for dinner.'
  'We can't make chips because we haven't got any potatoes.'

7 'What does your brother look like?'
  'He's tall with curly blond hair.'

8 Did you wrote any postcards when you were on holiday?

9 He usually wears jeans but today he's wearing a suit because he's going for a job interview.

10 'Does she live with her family?'
  'No, she lives in a flat by her own.'

11 My new car is more fast than my old one, but it's also more expensive.

12 You mustn't telephone me at work – my boss doesn't like it.

13 I never went to America, but I would like to go there soon.

14 I'm going to live in Barcelona for six months to learn Spanish.

STUDENT B

1 They've got one daughter and she's a doctor.

2 English is spoken by 350 million people in the world.

3 I go to work by bus and it only takes five minutes because I live very near of the office.

4 I like playing football but I've broken my leg so I can't do any sport at the moment.

5 I can't answer the telephone because I wash my hair.

6 'Let's have fish and chips for dinner.'
  'We can't make chips because we haven't got some potatoes.'

7 'What does your brother looks like?'
  'He's tall with curly blond hair.'

8 Did you write any postcards when you were on holiday?

9 He's usually wearing jeans but today he's wearing a suit because he's going for a job interview.

10 'Does she live with her family?'
  'No, she lives in a flat by herself.'

11 My new car is faster than my old one, but it's also more expensive.

12 You mustn't to telephone me at work – my boss doesn't like it.

13 I've never been to America, but I would like to go there soon.

14 I'm going to live in Barcelona for six months for learn Spanish.

PHOTOCOPIABLE

Find the mistake **Worksheet Progress check**   *36-40*

ACTIVITY
Pairwork: speaking

AIM
To identify and correct grammatical mistakes in sentences.

GRAMMAR AND FUNCTIONS
Revision

VOCABULARY
Revision

PREPARATION
Make one copy of the worksheet for each pair of students and cut it in half as indicated.

TIME
30 minutes

PROCEDURE
1 Divide the class into Group A and Group B.

2 Give one copy of Student A sentences to each student in Group A and one copy of Student B sentences to each student in Group B.

3 Ask the students to work with one or two other students from the same group. Tell them that some of their sentences are correct, while some of them have a grammatical mistake in them. They should decide whether the sentences are grammatically correct and make corrections where necessary. The students should discuss the sentences in their pairs or groups, but all the students should write corrections on their own worksheets.

4 When they have done that, ask the students to work with a partner from the other group (ie a student from Group A should work with a student from Group B). They should compare their sentences. Student A has the correct form of sentences which are grammatically incorrect on Student B's worksheet and vice versa. This means that the students should be able to correct one another at this stage.

5 Check that the students have identified the correct versions of the sentences.

ANSWERS

Student A		Student B	
1	incorrect	1	correct
2	incorrect	2	correct
3	correct	3	incorrect
4	incorrect	4	correct
5	correct	5	incorrect
6	correct	6	incorrect
7	correct	7	incorrect
8	incorrect	8	correct
9	correct	9	incorrect
10	incorrect	10	correct
11	incorrect	11	correct
12	correct	12	incorrect
13	incorrect	13	correct
14	correct	14	incorrect